Vocabulary Power Plus

Vocabulary, Reading, and Writing Exercises
for Higher Achievement

Level Eight

By Daniel A. Reed

Edited by Mary Beardsley

ISBN: 978-1-58049-267-6

Prestwick House
P.O. Box 658 · Clayton, DE 19938
(800) 932-4593 · www.prestwickhouse.com

Table of Contents

INTRODUCTION

Vocabulary *Power Plus* Levels Six through Eight combine classroom-tested vocabulary drills with reading exercises designed to prepare students for both secondary school and the revised Scholastic Assessment Test; however, *Vocabulary Power Plus* is a resource for all students—not just those who are college bound or preparing for the SAT. This series is intended to increase vocabulary, improve grammar, enhance writing, and boost critical reading skills for students at all levels of learning.

Vocabulary Power Plus reinforces each vocabulary word by presenting it in several different contexts. Words in Context activities allow students to identify the correct context for each lesson's words. Sentence Completion and Improving Paragraphs exercises foster writing and editing skills and prompt students to create contexts for words instead of simply memorizing definitions. Each exercise, including Prefixes and Suffixes and Reading Comprehension, is linked to the vocabulary list. Students receive additional reinforcement through review activities after every third lesson. Review lessons further the development of inference skills and highlight word relationships and shades of meaning.

We hope that you find the *Vocabulary Power Plus* series to be an effective tool for teaching new words and an exceptional tool for preparing students for secondary school and standardized tests.

Strategies for Completing Activities

Words in Context

To complete the answer for Words in Context questions, first read the entire sentence, and then focus on the words closest to the blank and determine the correct answer's part of speech.

If a noun precedes the blank, then the answer is likely to be a verb. For example:

> The repairman _____ an old sock when he looked beneath the dryer.

In this example, *repairman* is the subject of the clause containing the blank, and *sock* is the object. The sentence would become senseless if an adjective or a noun were used in the blank.

If an adjective precedes the blank space, then the answer is most likely a noun. For example:

> The tired _____ has been fixing dryers all day long.

The adjective *tired* must modify something. Using an adjective for the answer creates a nonsensical sentence. The answer cannot be a verb because the sentence provides no subject for the verb *has been fixing*. Placing a noun in the blank creates a subject for the sentence and provides a word for *tired* to modify.

Articles such as *a, an,* and *the* can also precede nouns, but you must look at what follows the blank to determine what type of word the answer will be. For example:

> The repairman fixed a _____ today.

In this example, the blank must be a noun, which serves as the object of the verb *fixed*.

> The repairman fixed a _____ dryer today.

In this example, the blank must be an adjective, because something must modify the noun *dryer*.

An answer's part of speech varies also when a verb precedes the blank. If a verb precedes the blank, first determine the purpose of the verb. Will the answer be the *object* of the verb, or a *part* of the verb? For example:

> The repairman fixed _____ dryers today.

In this example, the answer must be an adjective that modifies *dryers*.

> The repairman plans to _____ the dryer tomorrow.

In this example, the answer will be a verb that completes the infinitive phrase, *to*....

> The repairman will not _____ the dryer today.

In this example, the answer will be a verb that completes the verb phrase, *will not*....

Identifying the answer's part of speech will allow you to narrow the word list down to a few possible answers, but you must take into account the rest of the sentence to select the answer that best matches the context of the sentence. As you read, think about the context of the answer. Does the sentence have a positive connotation, or is it negative? Is it formal, or is it casual? Does it use language specific to a particular subject or field of study that would limit the answer to a specific word?

Sentence Completion

The main thing to remember about sentence completion is that your answer must show that you understand the meaning of the word. Your answer must *show* the word in use—not simply redefine the word. For example:

> When it landed on the floor after being dropped, the *flimsy* container...

The word is *flimsy*, which means *delicate* or *fragile*. To create your answer, first ask yourself what would reveal to you whether something is *flimsy*. In this sentence, the clue is already begun for you because the flimsy container has been dropped onto the floor. Determine what a *flimsy* container would do if it fell onto the floor, and write it:

> When it landed on the floor after being dropped, the *flimsy* container...shattered into many small pieces, spilling its contents everywhere.

Prefixes and Suffixes

Use the Words in Context strategy of determining a part of speech to decide the type of word you will need to complete each sentence. You must form the word you need by combining a vocabulary word with a prefix or suffix, which means that your answer will use the same root as the vocabulary word provided, if not the entire word.

To identify the answer, first consider the definition of the given word and how it relates to the topic of the sentence provided. Then, look over the prefixes and suffixes and select the one that creates the proper part of speech and usage for the context of the answer.

Critical Reading

Reading questions generally fall into three categories:

1.   *Identifying the main idea or the author's purpose.* Generally, the question will ask, "What is this selection about?"

In some passages, the author's purpose will be easy to identify because one or two ideas leap from the text; however, other passages might not be so easily analyzed, especially if they include convoluted sentences. Inverted sentences (subject at the end of the sentence) and elliptical sentences (words missing) will also increase the difficulty of the passages, but all these obstacles can be overcome if readers take one sentence at a time and recast it in their own words. Consider the following sentence:

> *When determining an individual's total worth to the team, one must first, and perhaps most important, consider the player's attendance record, since this suggests important information about the individual's degree of commitment and is a signifi-cant indicator of the player's priorities, which should place the team near the top; a dependable teammate will demonstrate dedicated allegiance to the team through persistent practice and support of other players.*

        If we edit out some of the words, the main point of this sentence is obvious.

> *When determining an individual's   worth to the team,*
> > *consider the player's*
> *attendance record, since this suggests*
> > *the individual's degree of commitment and*
> > > *priorities*
> > > *; a dependable teammate will demonstrate*
> > *allegiance to the team through   practice*
> *and support of other players.*

Some sentences need only a few deletions for clarification, but others require major recasting and additions; they must be read carefully and put into the reader's own words.

> Some in their discourse desire rather commendation of wit, in being able to hold all arguments, than of judgment, in discerning what is true; as if it were a praise to know what might be said, and not what should be thought.

After studying it, a reader might recast the sentence as follows:

> In conversation, some people desire praise for their abilities to maintain the conversation rather than their abilities to identify what is true or false, as though it were better to sound good than to know what is truth or fiction.

2.   *Identifying the stated or implied meaning.* What is the author stating or suggesting?

The literal meaning of a text does not always correspond with the intended meaning. To understand a passage fully, readers must determine which meaning—if there is more than one—is the intended meaning of the passage. Consider the following sentence:

> …an expression of courtesy and interest gleamed out upon his features; proving that there was light within him and that it was only the outward medium of the intellectual lamp that obstructed the rays in their passage.

Interpreted literally, this Nathaniel Hawthorne metaphor suggests that a light-generating lamp exists inside of the human body. Since this is impossible, the reader must look to the metaphoric meaning of the passage to understand it properly. In the metaphor, Hawthorne refers to the human mind—consciousness—as a lamp that emits light, and other people cannot always see the lamp because the outside "medium"—the human body—sometimes blocks it.

3. *Identifying the tone or mood of the selection.* What feeling does the text evoke?

To answer these types of questions, readers must look closely at words and their connotations; for example, the words *stubborn* and *firm* share almost the same definition, but a writer who describes a character as *stubborn* rather than *firm* is probably suggesting something negative about the character.

Improving Paragraphs

When you read a passage, remember that Improving Paragraphs exercises focus on the clarity and organization of the whole passage as opposed to single, confined, grammatical errors. Improving Paragraphs questions fall into four categories:

1. *Analytical.* This type of question involves the main idea, or organization, of the passage, and it might require you to understand the purpose or the meaning of the whole passage before you answer. Be aware of topic sentences, sentences that contradict the author's intention, and information that seems to be in the wrong place.

2. *Sentence Revision.* Revision questions focus on single, troubled sentences that either lack clarity or contain some other type of flaw. These sentences may or may not affect the whole paragraph.

3. *Sentence Combination.* Combination questions ask you to fulfill the purpose of existing sentences using fewer words, thus simplifying and clarifying the text. These can sometimes be identified during your initial reading of the text because flawed combinations distort meanings and create awkward paragraphs.

4. *Sentence Addition.* Addition questions present sentences which, when added to the passage or deleted from the passage, enhance the general clarity of the text. Watch for "loose ends" or poor transitions between paragraphs as potential areas for addition questions.

Pronunciation Guide

a — track
ā — mate
ä — father
â — care
e — pet
ē — be
i — bit
ī — bite
o — job
ō — wrote
ô — port, horse, fought
ōō — proof
ŏŏ — book
u — pun
ū — you
û — purr
ə — about, system, supper, circus
îr — steer
ë — Fr. coeur
oi — toy

Word List

Lesson One
aberration
bequeath
capitulate
debilitate
ensconce
felicity
glutton
hamlet
implausible
loathe
malice
nostalgia
pilfer
recompense
volition

Lesson Two
allusion
chronic
denunciation
embellish
ferment
haggard
ingratiate
lassitude
malign
philistine
ramshackle
sage
transcend
voluminous
wistful

Lesson Three
anonymity
awry
citadel
delirious
effervescent
fervor
hoard
kiosk
muster
partisan
prodigious
refurbish
sporadic
thoroughfare
venerable

Lesson Four
acclaim
bedraggled
cryptic
ebb
fanatic
haphazard
illuminate
legacy
maim
perceptive
repudiate
solicitude
taint
trepidation
waif

Lesson Five
assuage
blasphemous
celestial
dialogue
exuberant
heretic
incorrigible
peevish
portend
quash
reticent
squalid
turbulent
unorthodox
wrath

Lesson Six
alleviate
anthology
conciliatory
diminution
esoteric
grit
ludicrous
menial
pessimistic
phosphorescence
ransack
salvo
tentative
vicarious
yearn

Lesson Seven
arid
compatible
deplore
fraught
incontrovertible
loquacious
microcosm
ornate
petulant
quip
scoff
tantalize
urbane
volatile
wanton

Lesson Eight
apathy
bludgeon
cursory
eloquent
forlorn
innumerable
murky
ordeal
phoenix
rebuff
scrupulous
specter
textile
ultimatum
vanguard

Lesson Nine
amass
bravado
commiserate
deter
euphemism
fledgling
lavish
menagerie
occult
peripheral
profusion
recluse
skittish
tangible
undulate

Lesson Ten
amendment
calliope
clairvoyance
didactic
epic
gruff
incomprehensible
lurch
ocular
palatable
quiver
residual
stoic
tirade
voracious

Lesson Eleven
adversary
ambulatory
cacophony
capricious
cumbersome
exacerbate
hierarchy
insatiable
meander
overt
piety
rebut
squabble
treachery
validate

Lesson Twelve
ajar
buffoon
dexterous
engender
geology
impartial
malicious
nonchalant
pantomime
prolific
recede
sequester
tawdry
uncouth
vulnerable

Lesson Thirteen
acquiesce
cite
cynical
denote
dismantle
extortion
indignant
luscious
oppressive
ponderous
requisition
suffrage
unbridled
utopia
virtuoso

Lesson Fifteen
analogous
cleave
derogatory
distraught
exemplary
homogeneous
inadvertent
muddle
onomatopoeia
pompous
prowl
raze
stealthy
throng
vex

Lesson Seventeen
amiable
baleful
criterion
devoid
dormant
eulogy
iconoclast
instigate
marginal
peerless
prone
repel
serene
tactless
unfathomable

Lesson Fourteen
abstinence
annihilation
callous
delve
entrails
grapple
incipient
mandatory
obliterate
pliable
rummage
solemn
tedious
ungainly
vilify

Lesson Sixteen
anarchy
behoove
contempt
diffusion
elusive
fanfare
gullible
icon
mangle
oblique
patriarchal
recourse
sabotage
susceptible
usurer

Lesson Eighteen
assimilate
colloquial
dirge
epithet
festoon
hamper
induce
matriarchal
niche
perfidy
prophetic
rehabilitate
simultaneous
surmise
vigilante

Lesson Nineteen	Lesson Twenty	Lesson Twenty-One
antagonism	ardent	atrophy
aversion	cower	capsize
cavalier	devious	dearth
diatribe	doggerel	disdain
disencumber	imp	embezzle
evanescent	invalid	inept
gala	multifarious	iota
insignia	munificent	omnipotent
morbid	oracle	piecemeal
perturb	posterity	precipice
prosecute	pretentious	prostrate
spelunker	procure	relic
surreal	resilient	staunch
tyrannical	rivulet	sumptuous
unassailable	thwart	unscathed

Lesson One

1. **aberration** (ab ə rā´ shən) *n.* a deviation from what is normal or proper
   The restaurant's food is usually excellent, so the overcooked dinner was an *aberration*.
   syn: irregularity; abnormality   *ant: regularity; normality*

2. **bequeath** (bi kwēth´) *v.* to leave to another by will after one's death (law usage); to hand down
   Joe *bequeathed* the estate to the only remaining members of his family.
   syn: leave; bestow

3. **capitulate** (kə pich´ ə lāt) *v.* to surrender
   After realizing that there was no chance to win, the general *capitulated*.
   syn: cede; yield   *ant: endure; resist*

4. **debilitate** (di bil´ i tāt) *v.* to make feeble; to weaken
   A high fever *debilitated* him for a week.
   syn: devitalize; incapacitate   *ant: energize; strengthen*

5. **ensconce** (en skons´) *v.* to settle in a safe, snug, or hidden place
   Needing to rest for the night, she *ensconced* herself in a tiny cave and nodded off.
   syn: entrench; nestle   *ant: reveal*

6. **felicity** (fi lis´ i tē) *n.* 1. great happiness
   2. a pleasing manner or style
   (1) Gail enjoyed a day of *felicity* when she received an unexpected pay raise.
   (2) The *felicity* of the popular columnist's writing appealed to most readers.
   (1) *syn: cheerfulness; delight*   *ant: grief; misery*
   (2) *syn: gentility*   *ant: rudeness; offensiveness*

7. **glutton** (glut´ n) *n.* a person who eats or consumes to excess; a person who engages in a particular activity to excess
   Jerry does not care for burgers, but he is a real *glutton* for barbecued ribs.

8. **hamlet** (ham´ lit) *n.* a small village
   Wendy was eager to leave her tiny *hamlet* and venture into the world.

9. **implausible** (im plô´ zə bəl) *adj.* difficult to believe; unlikely
No one on the jury believed the defendant's *implausible* alibi.
syn: doubtful; improbable   *ant: credible; likely*

10. **loathe** (lōth) *v.* to dislike intensely
Max *loathed* waking up so early to do a job that he did not enjoy.
syn: detest; abhor   *ant: adore; love*

11. **malice** (mal´ is) *n.* a desire to cause harm to others
His *malice* endured for seven years as he plotted his revenge.
syn: ill will; hatred; spite   *ant: benevolence; gentleness*

12. **nostalgia** (no stal´ jə) *n.* a sentimental longing for things of the past
The antique car show is a source of *nostalgia* for many people.
syn: reminiscence

13. **pilfer** (pil´ fər) *v.* to steal, especially in small amounts
The archaeologist hopes to find the ancient treasure room before thieves *pilfer* all the artifacts.
syn: filch; purloin; rob   *ant: return; replace*

14. **recompense** (rek´ əm pens) *n.* payment in return for something, especially damages
     v. to pay or to pay for
    (n) The victim of the hit-and-run driver received no *recompense* for her injuries.
    (v) The king *recompensed* the victorious knights with many acres of land.
    (n) *syn: compensation; remuneration*
    (v) *syn: reward; compensate*   *ant: penalize*

15. **volition** (vō lish´ ən) *n.* 1. the ability to choose willfully
                               2. a choice; the act of making a choice
    (1) Her grades were excellent; she left the university on her own *volition*.
    (2) The type of career he pursues is not his parents' *volition*.
    (1) *syn: discretion; will; option*   *ant: coercion*
    (2) *syn: decision*

EXERCISE I – Words in Context

Using the vocabulary list for this lesson, supply the correct word to complete each sentence.

1. The jeweler is very cautious in hiring employees because several former workers have _pilfered_ valuables from the shop and then disappeared.

2. A leg injury _debilitate_ the player for the remainder of the season.

3. Many people drive through the _hamlet_ without even noticing the quaint apartments perched above the shops.

4. The engineer sounded an alarm when he noticed a[n] _aberration_ in the radiation levels around the nuclear reactor.

5. In the middle of the archery tournament, Jim _capitulate_ because there was no chance of earning enough points to win.

6. Joshua, a[n] _glutton_ for debate, spends hours arguing politics on his blog.

7. Watching the old, black-and-white movies evokes _nostalgia_ in Lauren.

8. On her own _volition_, Nicole stayed with the trapped victim and waited for the firefighters to arrive.

9. The doe _ensconced_ her defenseless fawns in a patch of tall grass.

10. Having no relatives, the widow _bequethed_ her vast art collection to a local museum.

11. Many people did not believe Meg's _implausible_ story until they read about it in the next day's newspaper.

12. The judge delivered a light sentence because he believed the defendant's crime was more a result of carelessness than true _malice_.

13. Courtney demanded _recompense_ from the car dealer when her brand-new car broke down.

14. They marked the end of the war with a day of _felicity_ and celebration.

15. Rachel _loathed_ speaking in front of others, so she tries to hide when the teacher calls for class participation.

EXERCISE II – Sentence Completion

Complete the sentence in a way that shows you understand the meaning of the italicized vocabulary word.

1. Brian's excuse for being late to school was *implausible*, so his teacher…
   gave him an infraction

2. Jose became angry when he learned that his father *bequeathed*…
   him less than his sister.

3. Since he was unable to control his *malice*, the boy was…
   put in time-out

4. Though Kelly expected no *recompense* for returning the lost wallet, the owner… gave her $20

5. An *aberration* in Ashley's classroom performance prompted the teacher to… give her an F and a mid-term

6. Four-year-old Kaitlyn *ensconced* herself in a pile of stuffed animals when… she was tired and cold

7. The worker *pilfered* products from the factory and then…
   got fired

8. Someone who *loathes* the outdoors would not…
   want to go hiking

9. She felt like a *glutton* after she…
   ate 3 servings of pasta

10. Samantha was overcome with *nostalgia* when…
    she saw an old photo of her and her brother

11. She *capitulated* to her opponent when…
    it was clear she was going to lose the game

12. The waitress knew that an appearance of *felicity* would…
    cause a gracious tip.

13. When a stomach virus *debilitated* Mark, he had no choice but to…
    stay home from school for the day

14. It was not her *volition* to move out of the house until…
    the price of the rent was raised.

15. She enjoyed living in the *hamlet* because…
    it was very peaceful and queit.

EXERCISE III – Prefixes and Suffixes

Study the entries and use them to complete the questions that follow.

The suffix *–ic* means "characteristic of" or "pertaining to."
The suffix *–ious* means "full of."
The suffix *–some* means "tending to."
The suffix *–y* means "quality of" or "condition of."

Use the provided prefixes and suffixes to change each root word so that it completes the sentence correctly. Then, keeping in mind that prefixes and suffixes sometimes change the part of speech, identify the part of speech of the new word by circling N for a noun, V for a verb, or ADJ for an adjective.

1. (malice)   The police forensics specialist must determine whether the death was accidental or the result of malicious intent.

   N   V   ADJ

2. (glutton)   Sick after eating an entire birthday cake, Larry wished he had not indulged in such gluttony.

   N   V   ADJ

3. (loathe)   Heather tries to finish her homework during the school day because she finds it loathsome to be indoors during such beautiful weather.

   N   V   ADJ

4. (nostalgia)   The advertisement claims that the collection of nostalgic music will transport listeners back to the 1970s.

   N   V   ADJ

EXERCISE IV – Critical Reading

The following reading passage contains vocabulary words from this lesson. Carefully read the passage and then choose the best answers for each of the questions that follow.

If you are a **glutton** for the outdoors, or you simply enjoy the thrill of finding hidden treasure, then know that geocaching (jee´-o-cash-ing) provides you with yet another excuse to disappear into the woods after school or on the weekend. All you will need is a little free time and a decent global positioning
5   system (GPS), which is now obtainable for less than one hundred dollars.

A GPS unit, often no larger than a cellular phone, is a device that can tell you exactly where you are on the planet. The device receives signals from orbiting GPS satellites, triangulates your position, and displays the coordinates for the
10   very spot on which you are standing (or floating or flying, for that matter). All GPS units provide the longitude and latitude of your location, and most new GPS devices include user-friendly electronic map displays and compasses. To go to a location, a user simply enters the coordinates of a target destination, and the GPS guides the user there in what is essentially a high-tech game of "warmer-colder."
15   The typical GPS will also track your average speed, distance traveled, and course.

Geocaching is soaring in popularity as GPS units become cheaper and easier to use. In this game, people **ensconce** geocaches, or weatherproof boxes, in secret locations, sometimes in public parks or just off the beaten path, and sometimes deep in the wilderness or high in the mountains. A geocache usually contains a
20   logbook, perhaps a camera, and an assortment of trinkets that can be left or traded by finders. Once the geocache is camouflaged just well enough to prevent non-players from accidentally finding it and **pilfering** the contents, the hider uses a GPS to acquire the coordinates of the box and then posts them on an Internet site for geocachers, such as *www.geocaching.com*.

25   If a GPS owner wants to find a geocache, he or she needs only visit a geocaching Internet site and then write down the coordinates of an interesting geocache. For nature lovers, there are thousands of geocaches hidden in the wilderness all over the world. Geocaching can be an urban experience, too, as many geocaches are hidden in cities. Some sites contain no actual geocache but simply mark a
30   historic or otherwise significant location.

Getting to a geocache ranges in difficulty from effortless to strenuous. Some geocaches might simply be sitting next to a parking lot, covered with leaves, while others might be dangling from tree roots on the side of a cliff. Do not worry about finding out the degree of difficulty when it is too late—each geocache listed on the
35   Internet usually includes a difficulty rating. Also, while GPS technology is always improving, few readings are exact; once a geocacher reaches the coordinates, a search might be necessary to find the hidden item, usually within a fifty-foot circle; however, if someone cannot find a geocache despite having arrived at the
40   coordinates, he or she can always **capitulate** and acquire more specific clues from the geocaching Internet site. Quite often, an **aberration** of the natural scenery, such as an unnatural pile of rocks, is the hiding place for a geocache. It is seldom

buried because players must access the geocache quickly enough to prevent non-players from seeing it.

45   Since items in a geocache are typically of little value, the real **recompense** for finding one, especially a difficult geocache, is the simple thrill of discovery and the refreshing (or strenuous) journey to the location. Logbooks allow finders to read messages from people who have found the geocache previously, and cameras allow finders to leave their images as proof that they visited. Some
50   geocachers are vacationers looking for a unique activity for the whole family, and others are hikers who simply enjoy the wilderness or its challenges. Geocaching is a relatively new sport, but it offers entertainment for everyone; there are plenty of caches for power hikers and extreme sports enthusiasts, and even more caches for people who simply want a good reason to take a pleasant stroll through nature.

1. According to the passage, which choice is *not* something that a GPS can calculate?
    A. average speed
    B. present position
    C. course
    D. cellular signal
    E. distance traveled

2. As used in line 17, *ensconce* most nearly means
    A. bury.
    B. hide.
    C. plant.
    D. place.
    E. leave.

3. Which choice is a requirement for someone who wants to participate in geocaching?
    A. a weatherproof box
    B. a flashlight
    C. a global positioning system
    D. access to private property
    E. a log book

4. As used in line 41, *aberration* most nearly means
    A. oddity.
    B. sign.
    C. exception.
    D. landmark.
    E. damage.

Q. The tone of the passage is best described as
A. indifferent and dismissive.
B. excited and skeptical.
C. distorted and purposeful.
D. mocking and playful.
E. frank and positive.

Lesson Two

1. **allusion** (ə lōō′ zhən) *n.* an indirect reference
   During his speech, he made an *allusion* to classical mythology by describing someone's efforts as being Herculean.
   syn: suggestion; hint   *ant: reference*

2. **chronic** (kron′ ik) *adj.* lasting and recurring for a long time
   They stopped inviting him to parties because of his *chronic* complaining.
   syn: continuing; habitual   *ant: fleeting; infrequent*

3. **denunciation** (di nun sē ā′ shən) *n.* open disapproval
   She resigned her position shortly after her *denunciation* of her employer's policy.
   syn: criticism; condemnation   *ant: acclamation; commendation*

4. **embellish** (em bel′ ish) *v.* 1. to make beautiful by decorating
   2. to improve by adding decorative details
   (1) She *embellished* the centerpiece with a dozen fresh wildflowers.
   (2) Henry *embellished* his fishing story so much that no one believed he had even caught a fish.
   (1) *syn: adorn; beautify*
   (2) *syn: exaggerate; aggrandize*   *ant: understate; minimize*

5. **ferment** (fûr′ ment) *n.* a state of agitation and excitement; unrest
   (fər ment′) *v.* to cause or to undergo a breakdown of chemical substances into simpler substances, especially sugar into alcohol
   (n) Management fired the outspoken worker for causing *ferment* in the factory.
   (v) The apples on the ground *fermented* beneath the hot summer sun.
   (n) *syn: uproar; commotion; turmoil*   *ant: peace; tranquility*

6. **haggard** (hag′ ərd) *adj.* appearing worn and exhausted due to overwork or worry
   Refusing to stop on the verge of discovery, the *haggard* scientist worked through his second night without sleep.
   syn: gaunt; fatigued   *ant: refreshed; invigorated*

7. **ingratiate** (in grā′ shē āt) *v.* to win favor with others
   He thought he would be promoted sooner if he *ingratiated* himself to the boss.
   syn: toady; flatter   *ant: alienate; irk*

8. **lassitude** (las´ i tōōd) *n.* a state of weakness and weariness
   Opal visited the doctor after experiencing *lassitude* for three consecutive days.
   syn: listlessness; exhaustion   *ant: vigor; vitality*

9. **malign** (mə līn´) *v.* to speak unfavorably about
                   adj. evil or harmful
   (v) The worker was fired when he *maligned* his company in a letter to a newspaper.
   (a) The sinister look in her eye revealed her *malign* intentions.
   (v) *syn: defame*   *ant: praise; extol; laud*
   (a) *syn: destructive; malevolent*   *ant: benign; benevolent; good*

10. **philistine** (fil´ i stēn) *n.* someone who is uninterested in or hostile to art or culture
                    adj. smug; ignorant
    (n) One of the members of the school board was called a *philistine* for suggesting that the school eliminate the music program.
    (a) She has the *philistine* idea that art and literature are simply wastes of time.

11. **ramshackle** (ram´ shak əl) *adj.* poorly constructed or maintained; rickety
    The *ramshackle* barn looked as though a strong breeze could blow it over.
    syn: dilapidated; decrepit; derelict   *ant: sturdy; solid*

12. **sage** (sāj) *adj.* sensible and wise
                  n. a person of celebrated wisdom or judgment
    (a) The successful stockbroker offers *sage* advice to people who want to invest.
    (n) As the most experienced doctor at the hospital, she is a *sage* to the young interns.
    (a) *syn: erudite; astute; prudent*   *ant: stupid; irrational*
    (n) *syn: guru; intellectual*   *ant: fool; ignoramus*

13. **transcend** (tran send´) *v.* to pass above or beyond the limits of; to be above or beyond the limits of
    True friendship *transcends* jealousy, so Lisa was happy despite having lost the lead part in the play to her best friend.
    syn: exceed; surpass   *ant: follow; trail*

14. **voluminous** (və lōō´ mə nəs) *adj.*   having great size or capacity
The students paled when they saw the *voluminous* book they had to read during summer break.
syn: capacious; sizable; extensive   *ant: scant; small; minute*

15. **wistful** (wist´ fəl) *adj.*   1. full of longing or desire
                                      2. sad in thought; pensive
(1) In a letter to his fiancée, the soldier expressed his love by quoting one of Shakespeare's *wistful* sonnets.
(2) The *wistful* student said very little and usually looked as though she were staring at something a thousand miles away.
(1) *syn: yearning; pining; desirous*   *ant: indifferent; unfeeling*
(2) *syn: melancholy; contemplative*   *ant: content; pleased; cheery*

EXERCISE I – Words in Context

Using the vocabulary list for this lesson, supply the correct word to complete each sentence.

1. She will suffer _chronic_ back pain for the rest of her life as a result of the injury.

2. He had such a[n] _philistine_ attitude that he would not attend the free classical music performance.

3. Grounded and confined to her bedroom, Allison released a[n] _wistful_ sigh when she saw the neighborhood children playing outside.

4. When Cody wrecked a car that he had borrowed, it caused legal _transcend_ between the two affected insurance companies.

5. After receiving poor service and terrible food, the critic _maligned_ the restaurant in her next column.

6. The negotiator asked the fugitive to _ferment_ his anger and free the innocent hostages.

7. The company's logo, a winged shoe, is a[n] _allusion_ to Hermes, the Greek god of messengers who wore winged sandals.

8. The prisoner enraged his comrades when he _ingratited_ himself to the guards.

9. Judging by her _haggard_ appearance, she had not slept for days.

10. The host of the talk-radio show claims to give _sage_ advice to callers.

11. The teacher hoped that a few minutes of jumping jacks and stretching would relieve the sleepy students' _haggard_.
    lassitude

12. She was once a member, but the group banned her after her public _denunction_ of its values.

13. The _voluminus_ SUV seats eight passengers comfortably.

14. The room looked barren and desolate, so Stephanie _embellish_ the walls with hand-painted vines and flowers.

15. Made entirely of sticks and palm fronds, the castaway's _ramshackle_ hut blew down when the first tropical storm struck the island.

EXERCISE II – Sentence Completion

Complete the sentence in a way that shows you understand the meaning of the italicized vocabulary word.

1. Brandy *embellished* her locker with… her locker decorations

2. Maggie's *allusion* identified the criminals without actually… saying their name

3. The leader of the mutiny *maligned* the ship's captain with claims that… he's a traitor and is feeding the enimies info

4. Leon must *transcend* his fear of criticism if he ever wants to… become a politican

5. The *haggard* man told rescuers that he… attacked by a sharkies worked until 12

6. His *chronic* drug addiction led him to… death

7. Many students stared at their desks in a state of *lassitude* after they… after they had too much sugar at the class party

8. The old *sage* advised his young apprentice to… focus on his studies.

9. Alicia made a *denunciation* of online banking after a hacker… broke into her online account and took money

10. Gary sparked *ferment* on the playing field when he… when the other team cheated

11. To Krista, the *ramshackle* bridge did not look… safe to travel across

12. The owner of the company *ingratiated* himself to local politicians so they… give the company good reviews so people shopped their

13. The aging widow becomes *wistful* whenever she… thought of her youth, children, and dead husbnd

14. The *voluminous* interior of the house surprised the visitors because… The family who owned it was poor.

15. The *philistines* on the city council voted to… elimante the circus.

EXERCISE III – Prefixes and Suffixes

Study the entries and use them to complete the questions that follow.

The prefix *de–* means "to remove" or "to reverse."
The prefix *dis–* means "not" or "apart."
The suffix *–ation* means "act of" or "result of."
The suffix *–graph* means "writing."

Use the provided prefixes and suffixes to change each root word so that it completes the sentence correctly. Then, keeping in mind that prefixes and suffixes sometimes change the part of speech, identify the part of speech of the new word by circling N for a noun, V for a verb, or ADJ for an adjective.

1. (transcend)   A hole in the canvas forced the hot air balloon to
   transcend

   N ⓥ ADJ

2. (embellish) While writing the incident report, the police officer
   disembellish the witness's extensive account so it included only the most
   important information.

   N Ⓥ ADJ

3. (chronic)   The runner used the chronicc on his watch to time his
   laps around the track.

   Ⓝ V ADJ

   chronicgraph

4. (ferment)   Grape juice will turn into wine if it undergoes fermentio n

   Ⓝ V ADJ

EXERCISE IV – Critical Reading

The following reading passage contains vocabulary words from this lesson. Carefully read the passage and then choose the best answers for each of the questions that follow.

It is no secret that television detective shows sometimes **embellish** the daily activities of investigators—why else would people watch the programs? The embellishments, however, have a few unwanted effects, according to court officials. Some prosecutors claim that jurors who are **chronic** viewers of criminal investigation programs are fed too many myths about investigators, and the myths create unrealistic expectations in real-world courts of law.

One of the greatest myths television perpetuates about investigators is the way they seem to **transcend** the time-consuming duties of real detectives. When television investigators search a crime scene, they find the crucial evidence in mere minutes, somehow spotting a single eyelash amidst the loose change, cat hair, and potato chip crumbs compressed beneath the sofa cushion. Realistically, the search of a crime scene might take days or weeks—even months! Imagine examining every tiny piece of lint on a living room carpet, or comparing the hundreds of fingerprints found on the counter of a convenience store. It is a tedious venture, to say the least, and far too tedious for forty minutes plus commercials.

Another common myth involves the equipment, technology, and specialized personnel available to most examiners. On television, the investigators bring the evidence back to a **voluminous** crime lab large enough to host a dodgeball tournament and filled with state-of-the-art computer terminals, put the materials through a series of high-tech, scientific tests, and have results by the next shift. Real investigators, some of whom work in **ramshackle** offices, are amazed by this portrayal, because evidence typically arrives at the lab and then takes its place in line behind hundreds of preceding cases. Why the holdup? Scientific testing takes days, maybe weeks, and usually months. A simple DNA test, for example, commonly takes longer than a week, even when rushed. Chemical tests, performed in minutes by actors, are often so complicated that they must pass through three or four specialists, each of whom works in a different city. Rarely—extremely rarely—does even a **sage** investigator have all the knowledge or expensive equipment necessary to conduct all the required tests single-handedly. Typically, crime labs are poorly funded and overburdened, and evidence must spend weeks simply sitting in the mail while being shipped from one specialist to another.

While most viewers understand that court television is fictional, many erroneously assume that the technical details—expensive equipment and abundant forensics specialists—reflect real-world conditions. This effect is minor, say prosecutors, until people having idealized images of the criminal investigation process are selected for jury duty. These jurors, who must eliminate any reasonable doubt before convicting someone, are demanding evidence that is simply unattainable by real-world capabilities. Certainly more money and time can supply more evidence, but technology does not always allow that to happen before the trial must proceed, which means that suspects must be released. Certainly, adequate evidence for conviction is a supreme necessity in a fair court system, but jurors must understand the limits and capabilities of investigators outside of TV-land; if not, real criminals will be free to walk the streets.

1. According to the passage, which choice is not one of the myths generated by court television?
   A. Case evidence is processed and analyzed immediately.
   B. Investigators are not always trained to perform the necessary tests on evidence.
   C. Crime labs are filled with state of the art, sophisticated equipment.
   D. The most recent case always takes priority over old cases.
   E. Evidence gathering is a relatively quick process.

2. The first sentence of paragraph 2 suggests that
   A. TV detectives accurately depict real detectives.
   B. the length of court television shows is limited by commercial advertisements.
   C. real investigations are exciting.
   D. TV detectives are exempt from the boring parts of criminal investigations.
   E. real detectives have easier jobs than TV detectives.

3. As used in line 18, *voluminous* most nearly means the opposite of
   A. spacious.
   B. interpretable.
   C. undersized.
   D. silent.
   E. exterior.

4. As used in line 28, *sage* most nearly means
   A. inexperienced.
   B. busy.
   C. careful.
   D. inconspicuous.
   E. wise.

5. The author of the passage would agree with which of the following statements?

   A. Sometimes the line between reality and popular entertainment is blurred.
   B. Most investigators do not know what they are doing.
   C. Television provides a fairly accurate depiction of real police work.
   D. Television has corrupted judges and prosecutors.
   E. Suspects should be considered guilty until proven innocent.

Lesson Three

1. **anonymity** (an ə nim´ i tē) *n.* the state of being unknown
The old hermit enjoyed a life of solitude and *anonymity*.
syn: obscurity; secrecy

2. **awry** (ə rī´) *adj.* 1. turned or twisted to one side
                          2. unexpectedly wrong; off course
(1) You can tell that he got dressed in a hurry because his tie is *awry*.
(2) The pleasure cruise went *awry* when pirates seized our ship.
(1) *syn: askew; crooked*   *ant: straight*
(2) *syn: amiss*   *ant: right; perfect*

3. **citadel** (sit´ ə del) *n.* a fortress
It would take an army to break into the *citadel* that stores the nation's gold reserves.
syn: stronghold; bastion

4. **delirious** (di lîr´ ē əs) *adj.* experiencing uncontrolled excitement, emotion, or confusion
The castaway became *delirious* when he saw another person for the first time in twelve years.
syn: feverish; restless   *ant: composed; collected*

5. **effervescent** (ef ər ves´ ənt) *adj.* high-spirited; lively
The children's audio book is narrated by an *effervescent* speaker whose voice conveys awe and excitement.
syn: animated; vibrant   *ant: dull; subdued*

6. **fervor** (fûr´ vər) *n.* feelings of intense emotion
Overjoyed with the thought of finishing his novel, the author wrote the final chapter with great *fervor*.
syn: passion; ardor   *ant: apathy; indifference*

7. **hoard** (hôrd) *n.* a secret supply for future use; a stash
                      v. to gather or accumulate discreetly
(n) The pirate's *hoard* contained the looted valuables from dozens of ships.
(v) The squirrel *hoards* nuts during the autumn to prepare for the long winter.
(n) *syn: cache; stockpile*
(v) *syn: amass; stockpile*   *ant: discard*

8. **kiosk** (kē´ osk) *n.* a small, open structure resembling a pavilion or gazebo

Keith had a summer job selling sunglasses from a *kiosk* in the shopping mall.

syn: booth; cubicle; stall

9. **muster** (mus´ tər) *v.* to call or summon together
   n. a gathering of persons for inspection

(v) The commander *mustered* the troops at 0600 hours.

(n) The students had to attend a *muster* in the lobby before they received their diplomas.

(v) *syn: assemble; rally*   *ant: disband; scatter*

(n) *syn: assembly; roll call*

10. **partisan** (pär´ ti zen) *n.* a strong, sometimes militant, supporter of a cause or group
    adj. devoted to a particular side or group

(n) The *partisans* refused to approve the new rule because it conflicted with their beliefs.

(a) The *partisan* bill gained overwhelming support from the Democrats, but none from the Republicans.

(n) *syn: advocate; zealot*   *ant: conciliator; neutralist*

(a) *syn: biased; predisposed*   *ant: neutral; impartial; dispassionate*

11. **prodigious** (prə dij´ əs) *adj.* 1. far better than or beyond average
    2. impressively great in power, size, or extent

(1) The *prodigious* author wrote three bestselling novels in two years.

(2) Construction of the 1500-mile Alaskan Highway was a *prodigious* undertaking.

(1) *syn: extraordinary; phenomenal*   *ant: average; typical; marginal*

(2) *syn: enormous; massive; vast*   *ant: small; scant; minuscule*

12. **refurbish** (rē fûr´ bish) *v.* to make bright, clean, or appealing again

They *refurbished* the old house and then sold it for double the price they originally paid.

syn: renovate; restore; renew   *ant: wreck; vandalize*

13. **sporadic** (spô rad´ ik) *adj.* occurring singly in scattered locations at unpredictable intervals

Scientists worried that a few *sporadic* cases of the deadly virus would be enough to start a worldwide epidemic.

syn: intermittent; random; periodic   *ant: consistent; reliable*

14. **thoroughfare** (thûr´ ō fâr) *n.* a main road or public highway
    In most states, vehicles driven on a *thoroughfare* must be registered.
    syn: passage   *ant: cul-de-sac*

15. **venerable** (ven´ ər ə bəl) *adj.* worthy of respect; respected
    Citizens throughout the nation mourned the death of the *venerable* leader.
    syn: august; esteemed; revered   *ant: disgraceful; notorious; dishonorable*

EXERCISE I – Words in Context

Using the vocabulary list for this lesson, supply the correct word to complete each sentence.

1. The _____ of comic books sometimes spills out from beneath Dustin's bed.

2. The teacher's _____ voice helps the first graders pay attention to their lessons.

3. Richard _____ the engine and eked another few years of use out of the old car.

4. The coach _____ the players after practice so they would all hear his announcement.

5. The small town holds an annual festival in memory of its _____ founder.

6. He knew something was _____ when he saw the damaged lock on the front door.

7. Visitors can get maps and information from the _____ at the entrance of the amusement park.

8. Because New York has two baseball teams, fans are usually _____ toward one team or the other.

9. Ryan did not mail the letter because he wrote it while in a[n] _____, and he knew that his feelings might change.

10. The _____ builders erected the bridge in a single month.

11. After writing the well-known book, the author still maintained her _____ because she considered her work more important than her pride.

12. Except for a few _____ showers, the weather was beautiful last weekend.

13. The _____ repelled invaders for three centuries before the perfection of the cannon.

14. Cody received a ticket for operating his unlicensed ATV on a(n) _____.

15. In his _____ state after the accident, the man could not rest until he knew that his children were safe.

EXERCISE II – Sentence Completion

Complete the sentence in a way that shows you understand the meaning of the italicized vocabulary word.

1. A *citadel* at the entrance to the city defends…

2. Fearing *sporadic* riots, the governor deployed…

3. Convinced that the end was near, the man *hoarded*…

4. The celebrity wished to return to the *anonymity* of her former life because…

5. The judge was accused of making a *partisan* decision in court because…

6. After Dave *refurbished* the old bicycle, it…

7. Karla panicked and became *delirious* when…

8. The *venerable* manufacturer has a reputation for…

9. Cindy knew something was *awry* at the house when she…

10. The *effervescent* personalities of his grandchildren caused Bill…

11. His *fervor* for charitable causes led him to…

12. The *prodigious* work crew built…

13. At the carnival, there was a *kiosk* in which people…

14. Instead of traveling the typical *thoroughfare* for the trip, Frank decided to…

15. Anyone who can *muster* the courage will…

EXERCISE III – Prefixes and Suffixes

Study the entries and use them to complete the questions that follow.

The prefix *non–* means "not."
The suffix *–ate* means "to become" or "to cause to become."
The suffix *–er* means "performer of."
The suffix *–ous* means "full of."

Use the provided prefixes and suffixes to change each root word so that it completes the sentence correctly. Then, keeping in mind that prefixes and suffixes sometimes change the part of speech, identify the part of speech of the new word by circling N for a noun, V for a verb, or ADJ for an adjective.

1. (hoard)   James realized he was a chronic _____ when he could not bring himself to throw away the cereal-box toy even though it was broken.

    N   V   ADJ

2. (venerable) They taught the children to _____ great thinkers and leaders, not pop stars or trendy celebrities of the moment.

    N   V   ADJ

3. (partisan)   Neither conservatives nor liberals objected to the _____ proposal.

    N   V   ADJ

4. (anonymity) The _____ author of the bestselling novel never revealed his identity.

    N   V   ADJ

EXERCISE IV – Improving Paragraphs

Read the following passage and then answer the multiple-choice questions that follow. The questions will require you to make decisions regarding the revision of the reading selection.

(1) Throughout the centuries, the word "Viking" has become synonymous with fur-clad, bloodthirsty barbarians in horned helmets who, wielding sword and battleaxe, cleaved their way through villages, castles, and cathedrals, plundering and burning at will. (2) Such description is exciting, of course, but it is largely a fairy-tale; the victims of the raiders were understandably **partisan** in the way in which they recorded history. (3) The Vikings did indeed **muster** their forces and conduct **sporadic** raids of coastal towns, but true Vikings—pirates and raiders—represented only a portion of medieval Scandinavian society. (4) The word "Viking" has since become a generic term for all medieval Scandinavians, and, in contrast to the long-lived stereotypes, certain elements of Viking culture were surprisingly advanced, notably in matters involving the rights of women. (5) At a time in which many cultures regarded women as property, Viking women enjoyed relative freedom and equality.

(6) When the men sailed off to raid villages or trade with other nations, Viking women ruled the homestead with considerable authority. (7) Vikings settled in Iceland and are thought to be the first European explorers to find North America. (8) Their primary responsibility was ensuring that food **hoards** lasted through the winter. (9) The duty seems unexceptional at first glance, but it was a **venerable** role in a region having long, harsh winters—so much so that upon death, Viking women were buried with the keys to the food stores as a symbol of respect for their importance.

(10) Women also managed farms, maintained the livestock, prepared food for storage, made medicine, and cared for the sick—a **prodigious** undertaking, especially since women were as young as twelve when they married. (11) Again, the tasks may seem servile to modern women, but the historical chauvinism in this case is offset by the economic freedoms that few other women enjoyed in one thousand. (12) A woman brought a dowry to a marriage, often consisting of livestock, furniture, or jewelry, and she retained ownership of it for the rest of her life. (13) If a woman died, her property was passed to her children—not her husband. (14) There is also evidence that some Viking women were merchants, and some even became wealthy from trade, though it is improbable that they accompanied the men on trade expeditions.

(15) Marriage among Vikings was not unique for their time. (16) Usually prearranged, a marriage was regarded more as a practical family alliance than a personal experience for the husband and wife; however, if a woman was matched with an abusive husband or a poor provider, she was free to divorce him simply by declaring her intent among a few witnesses.

(17) The Vikings' equal rights history might never surpass the popularity of the mythical pointy helmets and longships, but it is definitely a significant note in world history. (18) Perhaps, while fighting for their rights, the American suffragettes of the 1800s should have taken cues from medieval Scandinavians—it's difficult to argue with a person who has horns and an axe.

1. To make the paragraph more coherent, which should be deleted from paragraph 2?
   A. sentence 6
   B. sentence 7
   C. sentence 8
   D. sentence 9
   E. sentences 6 and 8

2. To clarify sentence 11, the writer should
   A. replace "one thousand" with "the year 1000."
   B. move it to follow sentence 15.
   C. combine it with sentence 12.
   D. move it to follow sentence 9.
   E. include details about the roles of men.

3. Which sentence logically follows sentence 16?
   A. There always had to be witnesses.
   B. Traditionally, in a prearranged marriage, the woman has little choice about whom she marries.
   C. For women, this degree of personal freedom was practically unheard of throughout the rest of the continent.
   D. The younger women clearly needed to have some way to escape marriages, especially since they had little say about whom they married.
   E. Women, though, had many more economic privileges than personal privileges, especially in the subject of ownership.

4. Choose the most appropriate title for the passage.
   A. Myths About Vikings
   B. Women and Trade in Northern Europe
   C. Scandinavian Women in History
   D. Vikings: The Egalitarian Barbarians
   E. Violence and Equal Rights

Review

Lessons 1 – 3

EXERCISE I – Inferences

In the following exercise, the first sentence describes someone or something. Infer information from the first sentence, and then choose the word from the Word Bank that best completes the second sentence.

Word Bank

voluminous	debilitate	aberration	ensconce
prodigious	sporadic	ferment	embellish

1. A knee injury forced Ryan to stay off his feet for several days.
    From this sentence, we can infer that the knee injury _____[ed] Ryan.

2. During the drought, firefighters rushed from one location to the next, extinguishing random wildfires that erupted without warning in the forest.
    From this sentence, we can infer that the wildfires are _____.

3. The suitcase was large enough to hold a small person comfortably.
    From this sentence, we can infer that the suitcase is _____.

4. Susan, who had never missed a day of school, was absent for a week.
    From this sentence, we can infer that Susan's absence was a[n]

    _____.

5. No one had seen the new sheriff, but by the time he was due to arrive, gossip alleged that he was ten feet tall, bulletproof, and rode a buffalo instead of a horse.
    From this sentence, we can infer that gossipers _____[ed] the description of the real, new sheriff.

EXERCISE II – Related Words

Some of the vocabulary words from lessons 1–3 have related meanings. Complete the following sentences by choosing the word that best completes the specified relationship. Some word pairs will be antonyms, some will be synonyms, and some will be words often used in the same context.

1. A *kiosk* is nearly the opposite of a[n]
   A. hamlet.
   B. sage.
   C. hoard.
   D. citadel.
   E. philistine.

2. The word that best contrasts with *sporadic* is
   A. chronic.
   B. haggard.
   C. venerable.
   D. ramshackle.
   E. delirious.

3. *Lassitude* is nearly the opposite of
   A. recompense.
   B. ferment.
   C. muster.
   D. thoroughfare.
   E. allusion.

4. *Pilfer* is nearly opposite in meaning to
   A. debilitate.
   B. recompense.
   C. ingratiate.
   D. hoard.
   E. loathe.

5. A *denunciation* of a person might also serve to _____ that person.
   A. bequeath
   B. recompense
   C. malign
   D. transcend
   E. muster

6. To *refurbish* a decorative item on which the painted designs have faded, one might need to _____ it with new designs.
   A. capitulate
   B. loathe
   C. fervor
   D. ferment
   E. embellish

7. *Wistful* is nearly the opposite of
   A. chronic.
   B. effervescent.
   C. aberration.
   D. implausible.
   E. sporadic.

8. If exhaustion or disease *debilitates* a person, then he or she might look
   A. implausible.
   B. voluminous.
   C. partisan.
   D. haggard.
   E. prodigious.

9. A *philistine* would not have _____ advice to offer to a young artist.
   A. awry
   B. sage
   C. nostalgia
   D. implausible
   E. fervor

10. *Felicity* is nearly the opposite of
    A. embellish.
    B. transcend.
    C. prodigious.
    D. fervor.
    E. malice.

EXERCISE III – Crossword Puzzle

Use the clues to complete the crossword puzzle. The answers consist of vocabulary words from lessons 1 through 3.

Across

6. They knew she was wearing a disguise because her wig sat _____.
9. The coach will _____ the team before announcing who made the cut.
10. Amber becomes _____ when she remembers visiting her grandfather for the last time before he died.
11. To her daughter, Leona _____[ed] the necklace that once belonged to her great-grandmother.
14. The team will not be successful if members fail to _____ their personal issues and learn to work together.
15. Karen demanded _____ from the driver who dented her new car.

Down

1. The children were told to stop playing in the _____ because a car might strike someone.
2. Though the car was of little value, the dealer refused to _____ by selling it for less than the asking price.
3. Trying to _____ herself with the teacher earned her the label of "teacher's pet."
4. During the television advertisement, the president of the spatula company _____[ed] the other spatula companies, claiming they made inferior products.
5. No one even tried to believe his _____ story about being abducted by aliens.
7. Other than _____ traffic violations, the small town has virtually no crime rate.
8. Children were warned to stay out of the _____ factory because it is likely to collapse.
12. While playing hide and seek, she _____[d] herself in the hedges at the front of the house.
13. His impassioned speech revealed the speaker's _____ for the subject.

EXERCISE III – Crossword Puzzle

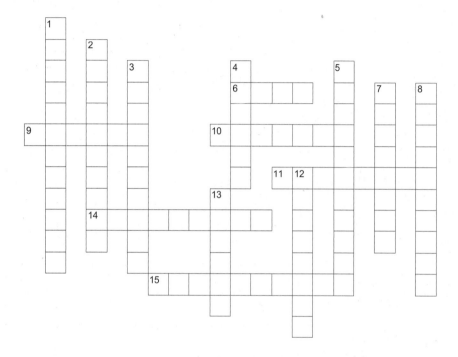

Lesson Four

1. **acclaim** (ə klām´)   *v.*   to approve or praise loudly
   n.   enthusiastic approval
   (v) To the delight of the owners, critics *acclaimed* the new restaurant.
   (n) The scientist's amazing invention received widespread *acclaim*.
   (v) *syn: applaud; extol*   *ant: deride; criticize*
   (n) *syn: applause*   *ant: disapproval; condemnation*

2. **bedraggled** (bi drag´ əld)   *adj.*   wet and filthy, as though having been dragged through mud
   Jack looked *bedraggled* because he was caught in a rainstorm while walking to school.
   syn: disheveled; unkempt   *ant: neat; dapper*

3. **cryptic** (krip´ tik)   *adj.*   having a hidden or secret meaning
   Few people understood the philosopher's *cryptic* messages.
   syn: mysterious; enigmatic   *ant: straightforward; frank*

4. **ebb** (eb)   *v.*   to flow or fall back, as the tide
   n.   a period of decline
   (v) The company nearly went bankrupt when demand for the product *ebbed*.
   (n) An *ebb* in viewer interest caused the network to cancel the once-popular show.
   (v) *syn: decline; recede; fade*   *ant: surge; increase; escalate*
   (n) *syn: recession*   *ant: surge; increase; rise*

5. **fanatic** (fə nat´ ik)   *n.*   one who has excess devotion to and enthusiasm for a cause or idea
   The *fanatics* camped in front of the ticket booth for two days in order to get the best seats at the concert.
   syn: radical; zealot   *ant: unbeliever; skeptic*

6. **haphazard** (hap haz´ ərd)   *adj.*   dependent upon chance; lacking any definite plan
   The safety inspector said that the factory's *haphazard* operation made it a dangerous place to work.
   syn: disorganized; unsystematic   *ant: orderly; organized; methodical*

7. **illuminate** (i lōō´ mə nāt) *v.* 1. to brighten with light
2. to make clear; to rid of confusion
(1) A row of lights *illuminates* the basketball court at night.
(2) The psychologist *illuminated* some possible reasons for the young man's disruptive behavior.
(1) *syn: light; light up*   *ant: darken; dim*
(2) *syn: clarify; enlighten*   *ant: confuse; complicate*

8. **legacy** (leg´ ə sē) *n.* something handed down from ancestors or history
The current generation enjoys the *legacy* set forth by the nation's founders.
syn: heritage

9. **maim** (mām) *v.* to disable or disfigure
A bull *maimed* a rider in a terrible rodeo accident.
syn: mutilate; wound   *ant: heal; mend; repair*

10. **perceptive** (pər sep´ tiv) *adj.* extremely attentive to sensory input; keen
The *perceptive* NSA agent finds hidden codes in seemingly ordinary messages.
syn: discerning; astute; sharp *ant: obtuse; slow*

11. **repudiate** (ri pyōō´ dē āt) *v.* to reject as untrue
The state had to drop the case when its star witness *repudiated* his previous testimony.
syn: deny; renounce; refute *ant: accept; acknowledge*

12. **solicitude** (səl is´ ə tōōd) *n.* 1. anxiety and concern
2. concern for the well-being of others
(1) After leaving for college, she called home twice a week to quell her parents' *solicitude*.
(2) His *solicitude* was an insult to the woman who had always refused assistance from everyone.
(1) *syn: worry; apprehension* *ant: comfort; calmness*
(2) *syn: consideration; attentiveness* *ant: negligence; disregard; abandonment*

13. **taint** (tānt) *v.* to corrupt or ruin by contaminating
The scientist *tainted* the laboratory sample when she touched it without wearing gloves.
syn: infect; pollute; defile *ant: clean; purify*

14. **trepidation** (trep i dā´ shən) *n.* a state of fearful uncertainty; dread
    He awaited the grade on his midterm exam with great *trepidation*.
    syn: anxiety; disquiet; unease   *ant: composure; equanimity; aplomb*

15. **waif** (wāf) *n.* a homeless person, especially an orphaned child
    The young *waif* sometimes sleeps in a tunnel beneath the highway.

EXERCISE I – Words in Context

Using the vocabulary list for this lesson, supply the correct word to complete each sentence.

1. They could not help feeling sorry for the _____ collecting alumi-
    num cans in an old shopping cart.

2. It is dangerous to walk in the outlying areas because of the _____
    placement of landmines during previous conflicts.

3. Two _____ children emerged from the wreckage of the house after
    the mudslide.

4. The fitness _____ sustains himself on protein shakes and clads
    himself in athletic apparel every day, whether he exercises or not.

5. The author hoped her new book would receive more _____ than
    criticism.

6. When the celebrity saw the article about herself in the tabloid newspaper,
    she _____ each of the reporter's claims.

7. Selena became angry when a fly _____ her sandwich by landing on
    top of it.

8. He _____ the cabin by hanging a lantern from the ceiling.

9. The treasure hunter spent a lifetime trying to understand the _____
    text on the back of the map.

10. The wood chipper nearly _____ the careless worker when he
    reached inside the machine to clear the clogged chute.

11. Vanessa was filled with _____ in the moments before the curtain was drawn for her first piano recital.

12. It took years for the nation to recover from the former dictator's _____ of cruelty and destruction.

13. Though nothing had obviously signaled danger, the _____ soldier knew that the platoon had just walked into an ambush.

14. When the crowd of fans _____, the celebrity will leave the concert hall and walk to the limousine.

15. The _____ of his family and friends helped Evan to recover quickly after the accident.

EXERCISE II – Sentence Completion

Complete the sentence in a way that shows you understand the meaning of the italicized vocabulary word.

1. The *haphazard* repairs to the plane kept it running just long enough for...

2. If the new television series receives little *acclaim*, the network will...

3. To relieve the passengers' *solicitude*, the captain...

4. The teacher *illuminated* the subject for students by...

5. The *bedraggled* man had just finished...

6. Ever since the harvester *maimed* the young farmer, he...

7. Crude oil *tainted* the water when...

8. A *legacy* of defeat hung over the tiny nation because...

9. The child became a *waif* when...

10. Some people believe that civilization will *ebb* if...

11. During the concert, a *perceptive* fan noticed...

12. *Fanatics* threw themselves on the ground in order to prevent...

13. Wayne *repudiated* Meg's claim that he...

14. It was obvious that the speaker was experiencing great *trepidation* because...

15. The *cryptic* message on the door could be understood by only...

EXERCISE III – Prefixes and Suffixes

Study the entries and use them to complete the questions that follow.

The prefix *de–* means "to remove" or "to reverse."
The prefix *in–* means "in" or "not."
The suffix *–al* means "pertaining to" or "characteristic of."
The suffix *–logy* or *–ology* means "science of."

Use the provided prefixes and suffixes to change each root word so that it completes the sentence correctly. Then, keeping in mind that prefixes and suffixes sometimes change the part of speech, identify the part of speech of the new word by circling N for a noun, V for a verb, or ADJ for an adjective.

1. (acclaim)   While campaigning for class president, Colleen _____ against the quality of the school lunches.
                        N   V   ADJ

2. (trepidation) Through threatened with physical harm, the _____ student refused to give any money to the bully.
                        N   V   ADJ

3. (fanatic) The _____ environmentalist chained herself to trees to hinder the lumber industry.
                        N   V   ADJ

4. (cryptic)   Anton's superior understanding of _____ allows him to decipher complex codes in a matter of minutes.
                        N   V   ADJ

EXERCISE IV – Critical Reading

The following reading passage contains vocabulary words from this lesson. Carefully read the passage and then choose the best answers for each of the questions that follow.

Miguel Hidalgo, called "Father of Mexican Independence," was a priest in the central Mexican town of Dolores. He was born in Mexico to upper-class Spanish parents, but he became an outspoken defender of Mexico's indigenous peoples, especially those who were poor. Though he won the **acclaim** of left-wing groups,
5   he was perceived as a **fanatic** by the government he sought to overthrow.

An enthusiastic reader of French revolutionary literature, Hidalgo was also a **perceptive** politician and an expressive public speaker. He used both his natural talents and the knowledge he had gained from books to stir up outrage from the peasants and *mestizos* (people of mixed indigenous and Spanish heritage) against
10   the Spanish king Ferdinand VII. In September of 1810, Hidalgo stood on the balcony of his church in Dolores and delivered a speech in which he urged the townspeople to revolt. The speech, which ended with the shout, "Long live Mexico!," came to be called the *Grito de Dolores*, or "Cry from Dolores." Since the name *Dolores* means "pain," the speech is also known as the "Cry of Pain."

15   The speech had an immediate effect. The peasants revolted, and Hidalgo urged them on in the name of the Church. To drive the Revolution forward, he chose for his banners the image of Our Lady of Guadalupe, a vision of the Virgin Mary that had appeared to an Indian peasant on a hill known as Tepeyac. She was a potent symbol for the indigenous Catholics, who considered her their own version of the
20   European Mary introduced by the Spaniards; the spot where she appeared had become a major destination for religious pilgrims.

Through the fall of 1810, Hidalgo won a series of victories against forces loyal to the Spanish king. In 1811, however, after a series of misjudged army maneuvers, he was captured by the Spaniards and forced, publicly, to **repudiate** the revolution-
25   ary movement. He was executed by firing squad in July 1811.

Although he was not a brilliant military strategist, Miguel Hidalgo was an exceptionally talented human-rights advocate—one of the first in the New World. He helped the oppressed native inhabitants of Mexico build factories and cooperative farms, and he advocated the abolition of slavery and the reapportioning of land
30   to native Mexicans. His **legacy** is one of freedom, courage and justice.

1.   In order to persuade the Mexicans to rebel against the Spaniards, Hidalgo
    A.   appeared to a peasant at Tepeyac.
    B.   became a human-rights advocate.
    C.   won a series of battles in 1910.
    D.   delivered the *Grito de Dolores*.
    E.   built factories and laid out farms.

2. Which choice is a synonym for *acclaim* as it is used in line 4?
   A. retribution
   B. approval
   C. justification
   D. condemnation
   E. protection

3. The best title for this passage would be
   A. The Religious Beliefs of Miguel Hidalgo
   B. From Priest to Warrior: the Life and Legacy of a Revolutionary
   C. Our Lady of Guadalupe
   D. The Beginning of Human Rights in Mexico
   E. Hidalgo and the *Grito de Dolores*

4. Hidalgo used the image of Our Lady of Guadalupe because
   A. it was an important symbol of freedom and justice.
   B. native Mexicans regarded her as representative of their culture.
   C. support for the Revolution was starting to ebb.
   D. he knew he was going to be executed.
   E. the *mestizos* were rising up against Ferdinand VII.

5. As used in line 24, *repudiate* most nearly means
   A. denounce.
   B. proclaim.
   C. reconsider.
   D. fight.
   E. criticize.

Lesson Five

1. **assuage** (ə swāj´) *v.* to make less severe or painful
   Her soft words temporarily *assuaged* the child's fears.
   syn: relieve; ease   *ant: aggravate; worsen*

2. **blasphemous** (blas´ fə məs) *adj.* disrespectful toward what is
   considered sacred
   Jack was a religious man, and he took offense when others made *blasphemous* remarks.
   syn: irreverent; profane .   *ant: pious*

3. **celestial** (sə les´ chəl) *adj.* of or relating to the sky or heavens
   Astronomy is the scientific study of *celestial* bodies.
   syn: heavenly   *ant: earthly; terrestrial*

4. **dialogue** (dī´ ə log) *n.* 1. a conversation between two people
                                  2. the lines spoken by characters in a literary
                                      work (e.g., a play or in fiction)
   (1) The old rivals engaged in a brief *dialogue* before the tennis match
        began.
   (2) The newspaper headline was borrowed from the *dialogue* of
        Shakespeare's play, *Hamlet*.
   (1) *syn: discourse; talk*

5. **exuberant** (ig zōō´ bər ənt) *adj.* 1. emotionally unrestrained and joyful
                                           2. lavish; abundant
   (1) Her *exuberant* expression relieved our fears of her being angry with us.
   (2) The dinner party featured an *exuberant* spread of gourmet delicacies
        from around the world.
   (1) *syn: enthusiastic; excited*   *ant: lethargic; weary*
   (2) *syn: plentiful; bountiful*   *ant: frugal; sparse*

6. **heretic** (her´ i tik) *n.* a person whose opinions conflict with established,
   popular beliefs
   Because the *heretic* openly questioned longstanding traditions, she was
   forced to leave the village.
   syn: dissident; rebel   *ant: conformist*

7. **incorrigible** (in kôr´ i jə bəl) *adj.* incapable of correction or
   rehabilitation
   The lengthy prison sentence simply gave the *incorrigible* man more time to
   plan for his next illegal act.
   syn: irredeemable; intractable   *ant: compliant; repentant*

8. **peevish** (pē´ vish) *adj.* easily annoyed; irritable
The *peevish* man seems to complain about every little thing.
syn: crabby; petulant   *ant: good-natured; easygoing*

9. **portend** (pôr tend´) *v.* to signal or warn of; to forecast
The sudden drop in temperature *portends* a tornado.
syn: foreshadow; herald; indicate

10. **quash** (kwosh) *v.* 1. to suppress with threat or force
2. to declare invalid
(1) The soldiers sent by the queen *quashed* the small uprising.
(2) The court *quashed* the unconstitutional ruling.
(1) *syn: crush; subdue*   *ant: enable; strengthen*
(2) *syn: nullify; invalidate; annul*   *ant: legalize; authorize*

11. **reticent** (ret´ i sənt) *adj.* disinclined to speak out; reserved
Bartleby, the *reticent* clerk, speaks only when there is no other way to communicate.
syn: restrained; taciturn   *ant: talkative; garrulous; chatty*

12. **squalid** (skwol´ id) *adj.* 1. filthy and miserable, as from poverty
2. morally revolting; sordid
(1) The woman and her fifty cats lived together in a *squalid* house.
(2) He argued that the *squalid* book at the library was like poison to the mind of a child.
(1) *syn: fetid; unclean; foul*   *ant: clean; sanitary; sterile*
(2) *syn: seedy; sleazy; repulsive*   *ant: decent; good; respectable*

13. **turbulent** (tûr´ byə lənt) *adj.* violently disturbed; chaotic
The Civil War era was a *turbulent* period in American history.
syn: tumultuous; riotous; unstable   *ant: orderly; peaceful; calm*

14. **unorthodox** (un ôr´ thə doks) *adj.* disregarding or defying tradition or standards
If typical treatment fails to cure patients, they might turn to a doctor who practices *unorthodox* healing methods.
syn: unconventional; alternative   *ant: conventional; traditional; accepted*

15. **wrath** (rath) *n.* intense anger that is often vengeful
Citizens feared the *wrath* of the ruthless dictator.
syn: rage; fury

EXERCISE I – Words in Context

Using the vocabulary list for this lesson, supply the correct word to complete each sentence.

1. Ancient astronomers observed the stars and planets in the night sky and drew _____ maps.

2. Molly becomes _____ and refuses to play anymore when someone beats her at her favorite game.

3. The movie's _____ was not realistic, because most people do not speak with such formality.

4. Her _____ teaching methods, some of which were never tested completely, drew skepticism from more experienced teachers.

5. Thought to be _____, the criminal was sentenced to life without parole.

6. Some passengers were tossed around in their seats when the plane flew through the _____ weather.

7. A free dessert _____ the customer's irritation over the poorly pre-pared meal.

8. Even when asked whether something was wrong, Travis remained _____ because he did not want to cause any trouble.

9. New proof of her innocence _____ the accusations against her.

10. According to her religion, it is _____ to work on the Sabbath.

11. When the officials saw the _____, unsanitary condition of the apartment, they took custody of the children.

12. He was called a[n] _____ for teaching philosophies that contradicted certain beliefs in his religion.

13. After accidentally breaking every dish in the china cabinet, the children tried to escape the _____ of their mother.

14. The dog's barking usually _____ the arrival of a visitor at the front door.

15. Fans let out _____ cheers when their team scored the winning goal with only seconds left in the game.

EXERCISE II – Sentence Completion

Complete the sentence in a way that shows you understand the meaning of the italicized vocabulary word.

1. The transition between elementary school and middle school can be a *turbulent* time because...

2. Friends *assuaged* her grief by...

3. The *exuberant* furnishings in the castle included...

4. As an exercise in history class, students were asked to write a fictional *dialogue* between...

5. If the king fails to *quash* the rebel forces, they will...

6. The *heretic* was put on trial for...

7. Unable to contain his *wrath* any longer, Ray...

8. With the election so near, the mayor became *reticent* about...

9. The ancient astronomers interpreted the *celestial* event as...

10. Her *blasphemous* remark angered...

11. Skeptics argued that the boss's *unorthodox* management style would...

12. The child becomes *peevish* when she...

13. Defense officials worried that the arrival of a single UFO *portended*...

14. The school district feels that the *squalid* imagery in the book is...

15. Immediately after his release from prison, the *incorrigible* thief...

EXERCISE III – Prefixes and Suffixes

Study the entries and use them to complete the questions that follow.

The prefix *pro–* means "in support of" or "before."
The suffix *–ence* means "state of" or "quality of."
The suffix *–ful* means "full of" or "having."
The suffix *–or* means "one who does."

Use the provided prefixes and suffixes to change each root word so that it completes the sentence correctly. Then, keeping in mind that prefixes and suffixes sometimes change the part of speech, identify the part of speech of the new word by circling N for a noun, V for a verb, or ADJ for an adjective.

1. (wrath)   The _____ victim of identity theft had to be restrained when he saw the criminal in person.

    N   V   ADJ

2. (turbulent) The new teacher experienced a period of _____ as she adapted to the students.

    N   V   ADJ

3. (dialogue)   During the _____ of the play, a narrator introduces the characters, setting, and situation.

    N   V   ADJ

4. (squalid)   The landlord evicted the tenant who lived in _____ because his filthy apartment attracted rats and cockroaches.

    N   V   ADJ

EXERCISE IV – Critical Reading

The following reading passage contains vocabulary words from this lesson.
Carefully read the passage and then choose the best answers for each of the questions that follow.

Bees! In their long history of association with humans, few insects have been more loved, more cultivated, more studied, or more essential to human existence. Bees, of course, help to pollinate orchards and gardens, but they also produce honey, which kings and emperors have declared tastes so good that it must be of a

5   **celestial** origin. Beekeepers, or *apiarists*, talk about the insects' social behavior and complex lives, and scientists have learned that bees can communicate the location of flowers by "dancing." People use bee products in shampoos and conditioners, eat honey for better health, and apply it to help heal minor scrapes or cuts. World honey production is worth approximately four billion dollars each year, yet it

10   is in danger in the U.S. because of two factors causing a reduction of domestic honeybee population: the introduction and spread of Africanized honeybees, and parasitic mites that prey on bees. Both of these were thought to **portend** disaster for America's apiarists, but only one does, and probably not the one you think.

Unlike common honeybees, which attack only if their hive is threatened,

15   African Honeybees are extremely quick to anger, swarm, and attack. These so-called "killer bees" were brought to Brazil from Africa as a way to increase honey production. Unfortunately, some of the bees escaped, established hives, multiplied, and began a so-far-unstoppable move into North America. Reports surfaced about their killing people in great numbers on their way north, and Hollywood

20   has produced a number of horror movies about the dangerous bees. One of the first films nearly caused panic by overstating the bees' tendency to attack or kill people randomly, but scientists were able to **assuage** public fears in the years that followed. The killer bees do exhibit **unorthodox** behaviors, such as mating with domesticated bees, frequently moving their hives, and not producing a lot of honey;

25   however, the bees, which were once thought to be the greatest threat to honeybee hives, have had a relatively small impact on humans and beekeeping.

The Varroa mite is the real cause of decline of a once-**exuberant** honey market. This tiny parasite actually lives on bees, sucking their blood and quickly killing them. The mite then moves on to another bee. In this manner, the mites can

30   destroy a hive in a very short time, turning a neat, orderly hive of a million bees into a **squalid**, chaotic mess. So far, scientists have not been able to **quash** the mites' attack on bees. Though beekeepers face financial ruin, they have been **reticent** in supporting the use of pesticides against the mites because of the possible ecological side effects. Miticides worked successfully for a while, but mites have since become

35   resistant to the chemicals, forcing scientists to explore different strategies. In addition, the aggressive nature of killer bees makes them less susceptible to the mites, so their numbers grow while domestic honeybees die off.

The situation is bad and getting worse—New Jersey apiarists estimated in

40   2005 that there are only two million wild honeybee colonies left in the entire U.S. This disastrous situation could cost America's beekeepers almost a billion dollars, but the problems do not stop there. Plants that require bees for pollination would

suffer, and this in turn will hinder food production. One government scientist pre-
dicts, "If honeybees ceased to exist, two-thirds of the citrus, all of the watermelons,
45   the blueberries, strawberries, pecans and beans would disappear."
Something must be done quickly to eliminate these mites, or the only bees we
might see in the future are killer bees.

1.   The word closest in meaning to *portend* (line 12) is
     A.   pretend.
     B.   bring.
     C.   cause.
     D.   invite.
     E.   predict.

2.   According to the passage, killer bees
     A.   migrated to the U.S. directly from Africa.
     B.   are just as dangerous as pictured in the movies.
     C.   present as much danger to humans as to animals.
     D.   are not as much of a threat to honeybees as Varroa mites.
     E.   do not mate with domestic honey bees.

3.   The parasitic mites kill bees by
     A.   spreading disease in the hive.
     B.   eating the young bees.
     C.   sucking the blood of the bees.
     D.   changing the atmosphere within the hive.
     E.   allowing killer bees to enter the hive.

4.   Which choice, according to the passage, is not an effect of the declining
     honeybee population?
     A.   economic loss
     B.   reduced food production
     C.   prevalence of killer bees
     D.   resistance to pesticides
     E.   inadequate pollination of plants

5.   As it is used in line 32, the word *reticent* means the opposite of
     A.   eager.
     B.   reluctant.
     C.   friendly.
     D.   positive.
     E.   miserable.

Lesson Six

1. **anthology** (an thol´ ə jē) *n.* a collection of short stories, poems, or plays
The English teacher issued each student an *anthology* of American literature.
syn: compilation

2. **alleviate** (ə lē´ vē āt) *v.* to make more bearable; to ease
The pill *alleviated* Susan's back pains.
syn: lessen   *ant: aggravate; worsen*

3. **conciliatory** (kən sil´ ē ə tôr ē) *adj.* overcoming distrust or hostility
through friendliness
His *conciliatory* manner helped to calm the angry customers.
syn: pacifying; appeasing   *ant: antagonistic; hostile*

4. **diminution** (dim ə nōō´ shən) *n.* a lessening or a decrease
Modern medicine has caused a *diminution* of deaths due to disease.
syn: reduction; attenuation   *ant: growth; increase*

5. **esoteric** (es ə ter´ ik) *adj.* understood by or meant for only a small group
Few of the books at the store suited her taste for *esoteric* literature.
syn: arcane; obscure; cryptic   *ant: mainstream; typical; exoteric*

6. **grit** (grit) *n.* 1. tiny grains of sand or stone
                          2. determination and courage
                v. to clench together, as teeth
(n.1) Be sure to remove any *grit* from the new sunglasses before you polish
them or else they will be scratched.
(n.2) In a display of true *grit*, the soldier ignored his injuries and carried
his friend to safety.
(v) She *grits* her teeth when she gets angry.
(n.1) *syn: granules; gravel*
(n.2) *syn: guts; nerve; backbone*   *ant: fear; cowardice*
(v)   *syn: gnash; grate*

7. **ludicrous** (lōō´ di krəs) *adj.* humorously absurd and nonsensical
The villain built a laser as part of his *ludicrous* plan to carve a gigantic portrait
of himself into the surface of the moon.
syn: ridiculous; preposterous   *ant: rational; reasonable*

8. **menial** (mē´ nē əl) *adj.* tedious and requiring little skill
She felt that it was too nice outside to finish the *menial* job of cleaning the basement.
syn: boring; humble　　　　　　　　*ant: exciting; remarkable*

9. **pessimistic** (pes ə mis´ tik) *adj.* expecting only the worst or most negative outcome
The *pessimistic* child usually gives up early because he is certain that he is never going to win.
syn: negative; cynical　　　　　　　*ant: optimistic; hopeful*

10. **phosphorescence** (fos fər es´ sens) *n.* continuous emission of light from a substance requiring neither heat nor sustained exposure to radiation
The tropical fish seemed to glow because of the *phosphorescence* of the chemicals beneath their colorful scales.

11. **ransack** (ran´ sak) *v.* to rummage and steal
The bears *ransacked* our tent and ate most of the food supply.
syn: plunder; pillage

12. **salvo** (sal´ vō) *n.* a simultaneous discharge of guns or cannons, or an outburst resembling such a discharge
The author endured a *salvo* of complaints just one day after her controversial book went on sale.
syn: barrage; bombardment; fusillade

13. **tentative** (ten´ tə tiv) *adj.* not definite or permanent
The *tentative* time for the program to begin was 8:00 p.m.
syn: provisional; indefinite　　　　　*ant: definite; certain; confirmed*

14. **vicarious** (vī kâr´ ē əs) *adj.* felt as if one were taking part in the experiences or feelings of another person
Grandfather's stories about his adventures in battle filled us with *vicarious* excitement and terror.

15. **yearn** (yûrn) *v.* to desire intensely, sometimes with sadness
The old man *yearned* to return to the simpler days of his youth.
syn: long; ache; crave

EXERCISE I – Words in Context

Using the vocabulary list for this lesson, supply the correct word to complete each sentence.

1. The date of the parade is _____ because the event requires good weather.

2. The _____ contains all the most popular American folk tales.

3. Three days of camping in the wilderness made Kayla _____ for a hot shower and a soft bed.

4. The children were given the _____ chore of drying the dishes.

5. Mayor West hoped that his _____ speech would prevent a riot.

6. The secret agent _____ the laboratory and escaped with the missile plans.

7. The engineers _____ pressure on the dam by allowing some of the water to flow through it.

8. Her _____ design for the mousetrap made use of clockwork mechanisms, pulleys, and heavy anvils.

9. The naval ship fired a[n] _____ at the pirates who refused to surrender.

10. The city hoped that hiring more police would cause a[n] _____ of crime.

11. The _____ of the mineral becomes apparent when the lights are turned off and the rock continues to glow.

12. Alyssa experiences _____ delights of parenthood when she babysits her many young nieces and nephews.

13. Though starving and sick with disease, the pioneers had the _____ to continue their 2000-mile journey.

14. Despite Kyle's _____ attitude, his team won the game.

15. Only a few scholars on the planet possess the _____ knowledge required to decode the ancient writing.

EXERCISE II – Sentence Completion

Complete the sentence in a way that shows you understand the meaning of the italicized vocabulary word.

1. According to the coach, only players who have *grit* will…

2. Many video-game players enjoy the *vicarious* thrill of…

3. The child has a *ludicrous* belief that…

4. The teacher wanted to use an *anthology* because…

5. After enduring a *salvo* of water balloons, the wet victim…

6. A shopping cart will *alleviate* the burden of…

7. Their vacation plans will be *tentative* until…

8. The *phosphorescence* of the numbers on his watch allows…

9. In a *conciliatory* voice, the game show host told the contestant…

10. Ralph prefers *esoteric* music to the sounds of…

11. Though she loved rooming with her sister, Lydia *yearned* for her own bedroom because…

12. The *menial* job was difficult only because…

13. Police serving a search warrant *ransacked*…

14. The *pessimistic* man was surprised when…

15. The speaker waited for a *diminution* of applause before…

EXERCISE III – Prefixes and Suffixes

Study the entries and use them to complete the questions that follow.

The suffix –*ent* means "performer of," "doing," or "causing."
The suffix –*ion* means "act of," "state of," or "result of."
The suffix –*ism* means "system" or "system of."
The suffix –*ive* means "tending to be."

Use the provided prefixes and suffixes to change each root word so that it completes the sentence correctly. Then, keeping in mind that prefixes and suffixes sometimes change the part of speech, identify the part of speech of the new word by circling N for a noun, V for a verb, or ADJ for an adjective.

1. (pessimistic) Jeremy doubted whether the escape plan would work, but he kept his _____ private because he did not want to cause a panic among the other people stuck in the elevator.

    N V ADJ

2. (diminution) The archaeologist asked the _____ guide to crawl into the tiny cave opening to search for clues.

    N V ADJ

3. (phosphorescence) The _____ keychain is easy to find in the dark.

    N V ADJ

4. (alleviate) To gain temporary _____ from the painful burn, Eric put his hand in the ice-filled cooler.

    N V ADJ

EXERCISE IV – Improving Paragraphs

Read the following passage and then answer the multiple-choice questions that follow. The questions will require you to make decisions regarding the revision of the reading selection.

(1) The first wanderers to pass through Racetrack Playa were probably too hot and thirsty to be concerned about some strange rocks; after all, the temperature in Death Valley, California, regularly exceeds 120 degrees. (2) To a slow-cooked brain, the mysterious furrows trailing quarter-ton boulders in the middle of a dry, cracked lakebed might have registered as a peculiar, if not amusing, mirage. (3) The trails, however, were quite real, and the Sliding Boulders of Playa have become yet another topic in **anthologies** of unsolved mysteries of the natural world.

(4) Racetrack Playa is a dry lakebed that extends for three miles through the west-central mountains of Death Valley, and water is scarce and vegetation is sparse because the cracked mud receives an average of three-to-four inches of rain per year, usually during spring and winter. (5) The rocks that dot the landscape, though, are an attraction for tourists and scientists alike. (6) Grooves, seemingly "plow" marks through the hard, dry mud, extend from certain rocks as far as six hundred feet, as though some unseen force pushed them across the plain. (7) No one has witnessed a rock in motion, but there is no doubt that they move, because the weather quickly erases the furrows and new ones appear when the rocks move again. (8) The phenomenon is sporadic; some rocks sit motionless for years, and then move a hundred feet in one day. (9) Several explanations have been offered, from **ludicrous** theories of alien activity to complicated theories understood only by scientists having **esoteric** knowledge of geological electromagnetism.

(10) Since the mud on the playa is a very fine **grit** that expands and becomes very slippery when wet, and the trails typically extend in the direction of the prevailing wind, which sometimes rockets across the playa at speeds of ninety miles an hour, some scientists believe that the top layer of mud becomes so slippery when damp that strong gusts of wind are able to blow the rocks around.

(11) Some scientists accept the mud-and-wind theory as **tentative**, because they believe something more, presumably an ice floe, is needed to move boulders weighing hundreds of pounds. (12) They insist that ice floes cause the rocks to move. (13) It is conceivable, they say, that a layer of ice forms over the slippery mud during winter conditions. (14) The ice reduces the friction between a boulder and the ground, and an ice floe pushing against itself as it freezes (an immeasurable force that can split concrete sidewalks in half) will carry with it any boulder that happens to be sitting in the floe. (15) Rocks of different weight that move in identical paths seem to support the theory; two rocks being carried in the same ice floe would exhibit such parallel motion.

(16) Whether the rocks are moved by ice, blown by wind, or pushed by invisible elves, Racetrack Playa will continue to be a mystical place on its own characteristics. (17) Those who **yearn** to learn the secret of the rocks are also moved by the peace and silence of the playa. (18) Simply standing on the center of the playa and imagining the former lake, when it hosted countless animals and sustained native peoples of Death Valley, is enough to make the strange boulders seem irrelevant.

1. Choose the best revision for sentence 4.
    A. ...mountains of Death Valley. Water is scarce and...
    B. ...mountains of Death Valley where water is scarce and...
    C. ...mountains of Death Valley, although water is scarce and...
    D. ...mountains of Death Valley and water is scarce and...
    E. ...mountains of Death Valley because water is scarce and...

2. If inserted to follow sentence 9, which sentence would improve the transition between paragraphs 2 and 3?
    A. Since the UFO theories are not often discussed, they are the most likely.
    B. Certainly, more evidence will appear which supports theories of electromagnetic disturbances.
    C. So far, the best theories seem to be the simplest ones.
    D. The best theory that scientists offer is based on the fact that strong winds from the mountains push the heavy rocks across the slippery mud.
    E. When someone sees how the rocks move, they will not be nearly as interesting.

3. Which unnecessary sentence of paragraph 4 should be deleted?
    A. sentence 11
    B. sentence 12
    C. sentence 13
    D. sentence 14
    E. sentence 15

4. If the author wanted to lengthen the passage, which details could be included without interfering with the main idea?
    A. the daily life of people indigenous to Death Valley
    B. how to prepare for a hike through Death Valley
    C. the composition and makeup of specific boulders
    D. how the weather of Death Valley compares to other dry lakebeds in California
    E. a brief history of Racetrack Playa

Review

Lessons 4 – 6

EXERCISE I – Inferences

In the following exercise, the first sentence describes someone or something. Infer information from the first sentence, and then choose the word from the Word Bank that best completes the second sentence.

Word Bank

perceptive	esoteric	turbulent	pessimistic
unorthodox	menial	exuberant	ludicrous

1. The team had lost so many times that no one in the stands expected them to win.
   From this passage, we can infer that the fans are _____.

2. Kelly can tell exactly which state people are from by listening to the subtle differences in their speech.
   From this sentence, we can infer that Kelly is _____.

3. Michelle's management techniques seemed to work well, but they violated many traditional rules of good leadership.
   From this sentence, we can infer that Michelle uses _____ techniques.

4. During the Great Depression, millionaires became paupers overnight.
   From this sentence, we can infer that the Great Depression was a[n] _____ time.

5. The band's unique sound is appealing to a limited group of fans.
   From this sentence, we can infer that the band's music is _____.

EXERCISE II – Related Words

Some of the vocabulary words from lessons 4–6 have related meanings. Complete the following sentences by choosing the word that best completes the specified relationship. Some word pairs will be antonyms, some will be synonyms, and some will be words often used in the same context.

1. Her *haphazard* schedule is full of _____ events that might or might not happen.
    A. bedraggled
    B. perceptive
    C. blasphemous
    D. reticent
    E. tentative

2. *Ebb* is most synonymous with
    A. fanatic.
    B. diminution.
    C. taint.
    D. ransack.
    E. vicarious.

3. A severe infestation of mold *tainted* every object in the _____ house.
    A. squalid.
    B. esoteric.
    C. perceptive.
    D. vicarious.
    E. menial.

4. A *heretic* might be punished for speech that is considered
    A. pessimistic.
    B. tentative.
    C. acclaim.
    D. dialogue.
    E. blasphemous.

5. *Esoteric* is most synonymous with
    A. salvo.
    B. cryptic.
    C. turbulent.
    D. peevish.
    E. vicarious.

6. Receiving *acclaim* is preferable to experiencing
   A. dialogue.
   B. grit.
   C. wrath.
   D. phosphorescence.
   E. ebb.

7. If someone *repudiates* a new rule, then he or she might also want to
   _____ it.
   A. acclaim
   B. quash
   C. portend
   D. yearn
   E. illuminate

8. *Alleviate* is closest in meaning to
   A. portend
   B. ransack.
   C. taint.
   D. assuage.
   E. acclaim.

9. The natural *phosphorescence* of the moss _____ the cave well
   enough for the explorers to walk without using a lantern.
   A. assuaged
   B. quashed
   C. alleviated
   D. yearned
   E. illuminated

10. *Exuberant* contrasts most with
   A. perceptive.
   B. pessimistic.
   C. squalid.
   D. esoteric.
   E. vicarious.

EXERCISE III – Crossword Puzzle

Use the clues to complete the crossword puzzle. The answers consist of vocabulary words from lessons 4 through 6.

Across

1. In the heat and filth of the engine room, the _____ crew struggled to keep the ship's engine running during the battle.
4. If used improperly, a lawnmower can _____ its user.
6. The odor from the onions _____[ed] all the other food in the refrigerator.
7. Citizens of the impoverished nation _____ for a better life for their children.
10. She knew that the world was not yet ready for her _____ ideas.
12. The poem was a[n] _____ account of a cow jumping over the moon.
14. He became _____ with his critics when he realized that he had been wrong from the start.
15. The fourth-generation farm family abandoned its agricultural _____ and began selling real estate.

Down

2. To prevent a war, the starship commander opened a[n] _____ with the hostile aliens and tried to settle their differences.
3. A[n] _____ in demand for the product resulted in lower sale prices.
5. A[n] _____ person does not learn from his or her mistakes.
8. The _____ student seldom comments on anything.
9. A round of free appetizers _____[ed] most of the customers' complaints that the food was taking too long.
11. She found a[n] _____ summer job that required no special skills or training.
13. The children _____[ed] the house in search of the hidden cookie jar.

EXERCISE III – Crossword Puzzle

Lesson Seven

1. **arid** (ar´id) *adj.* lacking water or rainfall; very dry
    Dust clouds occasionally drifted across the *arid* fields.
    syn: baked; parched   *ant: humid; damp; wet*

2. **compatible** (kəm pat´ə bəl) *adj.* capable of existing or working together
    The project progressed smoothly because the workers had *compatible* personalities.
    syn: agreeable; congruent   *ant: conflicting; different*

3. **deplore** (di plôr´) *v.* 1. to condemn
                          2. to regret
    (1) Most people *deplore* the thought of children working in coal mines.
    (2) He *deplores* his former life of crime because it hurt so many people.
    (1) *syn: censure; criticize*   *ant: praise; support*
    (2) *syn: lament; bewail*   *ant: celebrate; rejoice*

4. **fraught** (frôt) *adj.* 1. filled with; laden
                     2. emotionally distressed or distressing
    (1) The dark forest is *fraught* with danger after sunset.
    (2) It took all the general's strength to bite his tongue during the *fraught* peace negotiations.
    (1) *syn: bristling; burdened; abounding*   *ant: lacking; devoid; empty*
    (2) *syn: frantic; frenetic; intense; upsetting* *ant: calm; soothing*

5. **incontrovertible** (in kon trə vûr´tə bəl) *adj.* impossible to dispute or
    disprove
    The crafty lawyer won the case despite the *incontrovertible* evidence that his client was guilty.
    syn: irrefutable; unquestionable   *ant: disputable, debatable*

6. **loquacious** (lō kwā´shəs) *adj.* talkative
    Sandy found it difficult to end the conversation with her *loquacious* neighbor.
    syn: garrulous; chatty   *ant: quiet; reserved; taciturn*

7. **microcosm** (mī´krə koz əm) *n.* a small part that represents the whole
    of a system
    Because of its diverse population, the small nation could be considered a *microcosm* of the world.
                                  ant: macrocosm; entirety

8. **ornate** (ôr nāt´) *adj.* richly and elaborately decorated
The antique grandfather clock was covered with *ornate* woodwork.
syn: elaborate; embellished   *ant: plain; stark; simple*

9. **petulant** (pech´ ə lənt) *adj.* easily annoyed; peevish
Carol admits that she is a *petulant* person until she has had her first cup of coffee.
syn: grouchy; irritable   *ant: easygoing; relaxed*

10. **quip** (kwip) *n.* a witty remark, sometimes sarcastic
              v. to make a witty or clever remark
(n) It seems as though every comedy television show must end with a silly *quip.*
(v) The two brothers humorously *quipped* back and forth whenever they met.
(n) *syn: one-liner; witticism; epigram*
(v) *syn: joke; jest*

11. **scoff** (skôf) *v.* to mock with contempt
The dealer *scoffed* at the customer's offer to pay half the asking price for the used car.
syn: ridicule; deride   *ant: praise*

12. **tantalize** (tan´ tə līz) *v.* to excite by flaunting a desired thing and keeping it just out of reach
He *tantalized* the dog by waving a piece of bacon high over its head.
syn: tease; tempt; entice

13. **urbane** (ûr bān´) *adj.* polite and refined in manner, as from vast social experience
He was such an *urbane* gentleman that she felt awkward in his presence.
syn: debonair; suave; sophisticated   *ant: crude; uncouth*

14. **volatile** (vol´ ə təl) *adj.* tending to change suddenly; explosively unstable
Anger management classes helped her to control her *volatile* temper.
syn: impulsive; precarious; explosive   *ant: stable; constant; unwavering*

15. **wanton** (won´tən) *adj.*   1. wastefully excessive
2. reckless and indifferent toward morality, decency, or justice

(1) Her *wanton* spending brought the family to the verge of bankruptcy.
(2) He thought that he had put his *wanton* lifestyle behind him, but it resurfaced when his employer found his criminal record during a background check.

(1) *syn: gratuitous; needless*   *ant: essential; crucial; needed*
(2) *syn: shameless; dissolute; immoral*   *ant: decent; upright; good*

EXERCISE I – Words in Context

Using the vocabulary list for this lesson, supply the correct word to complete each sentence.

1. Certain watchdog groups monitor the government to limit the _____ use of taxpayers' money.

2. The plant can survive in _____ environments because it requires little water.

3. Everyone in the office tries to avoid working with the _____ clerk because he complains about everything.

4. The term paper must be rewritten because it is _____ with errors.

5. The _____ woman spoke with the elegance and experience of an international ambassador.

6. In order to foster learning, the _____ child must sometimes be separated from the other students during class.

7. She _____ at his suggestion to share her bread after everyone refused to help her bake it.

8. The queen's _____ crown is decorated with relief carvings and gem-stones.

9. The new game is not _____ with the old computer's slow operating system.

10. A rivalry between the two teams caused a[n] _____ atmosphere in the stands.

11. A ridiculous _____ was printed in large letters on the front of his T-shirt.

12. He _____ the use of violence, except in self-defense.

13. It is hard to win an argument with Ken because he believes that his points are _____.

14. Photographs of mouth-watering meals _____ customers as they wait for seats in the restaurant.

15. A large corporation is sometimes viewed as a[n] _____ of society because it has its own rules and government.

EXERCISE II – Sentence Completion

Complete the sentence in a way that shows you understand the meaning of the italicized vocabulary word.

1. The used parts from the junkyard were not *compatible* with Ed's car, so he...

2. Whenever he receives unwanted phone calls, the *petulant* man...

3. The *volatile* chemicals are dangerous to transport because...

4. The people in the shelter were *fraught* with fear during...

5. The huge billboard for the fast-food restaurant *tantalized* customers with...

6. Macy wanted to take a nap, but the *loquacious* passenger sitting next to her insisted...

7. The suspect *scoffed* at the police when they accused...

8. Inhabitants of the *arid* region rarely...

9. Authorities reduced the *wanton* smuggling of drugs into schools by...

10. By studying a *microcosm* of the society, scientists learned...

11. Gianna took offense at the salesman's *quip* about...

12. The scientist's theory became *incontrovertible* when...

13. Eva *deplores* the use of foul language, so she...

14. The teenager spoke with the *urbane* refinement of a person who...

15. The *ornate*, wrought-iron gate at the entrance of the estate suggested...

EXERCISE III – Prefixes and Suffixes

Study the entries and use them to complete the questions that follow.

The prefix *in–* means "in" or "not."
The suffix *–able* means "able to be."
The suffix *–ic* means "characteristic of" or "pertaining to."
The suffix *–ity* means "state of" or "quality of."

Use the provided prefixes and suffixes to change each root word so that it completes the sentence correctly. Then, keeping in mind that prefixes and suffixes sometimes change the part of speech, identify the part of speech of the new word by circling N for a noun, V for a verb, or ADJ for an adjective.

1. (volatile)   The _____ of the stock market dissuaded the most cautious investors.

    N   V   ADJ

2. (compatible) The software for Sondra's new PDA is _____ with her old notebook computer, so she will need to download an update.

    N   V   ADJ

3. (microcosm) Longtime residents of the small town assumed that life there was a[n] _____ sample of life everywhere in the country.

    N   V   ADJ

4. (deplore)   Firing his own friend was the most _____ decision of Ralph's career.

    N   V   ADJ

EXERCISE IV – Critical Reading

*The following reading passage contains vocabulary words from this lesson.
Carefully read the passage and then choose the best answers for each of the questions that follow.*

In 1951, Ralph Baer's managers told him to design the best television set ever. The young engineer suggested some type of interactive game built into the television. Ralph's superiors **scoffed** at the idea and ordered him to stick to the basics. Fifteen years later, while working for a new company, Ralph revisited his idea for a
5   television-based game. On his own, he manipulated a television so that two bright squares on the television screen—dots, actually—could be controlled by the viewer. Baer's superiors felt that he was on to something and funded the project for the next few years. In 1972, the Odyssey emerged as the first home video game system.
During a show featuring the Odyssey, an engineer named Nolan Bushnell played
10   Baer's games. Within a year, Bushnell released the first coin-operated arcade game, *Computer Space*. After founding Atari, Bushnell introduced *Pong* in 1972. In 1975, Atari released a home version of *Pong* and accelerated the home video game industry.
During the late 1970s and early 1980s, video arcades emerged to **tantalize**
15   players with various games such as *Pac Man*, *Donkey Kong*, and *Galaga*. One quarter bought a player a few minutes of bliss at the helm of the high-tech machines. Many players had home systems, such as the Atari 2600, but at the dawn of video games, coin-operated arcade games featured better graphics and sound than their home-system counterparts; because of their large size and income potential, arcade
20   games were able to contain better and more expensive electronics than home systems.
In 1982, Atari learned that the video game industry could be **volatile**. Home video games stopped selling, but not before Atari produced mass quantities of game cartridges. Prices plummeted in a market **fraught** with quickly produced, low-
25   quality games that no one wanted to play. For three years, the video game industry virtually halted; retailers believed that consumers were simply no longer interested in video games.
Blaming mediocre games for Atari's demise, a small company called Nintendo dedicated itself to making games that were fun to play. In 1985, it released the
30   Nintendo Entertainment System (NES). Its flagship game, *Super Mario Bros.*, starred the same plumber who previously battled Donkey Kong. Skeptical retailers were at first hesitant to carry the product, but massive sales figures were **incontrovertible** proof that the video game industry was not extinct.
Nintendo's games sold by the millions, and other companies flocked to make
35   games for the NES to cash in on the craze. To avoid the same fate as Atari, Nintendo used harsh business practices to enforce tight quality controls on outside companies creating games for the NES. Game developers **deplored** the strictures, but they could not take their games elsewhere because Nintendo had no real competition.
40   In the early 1990s, Sega introduced the Genesis system to compete with Nintendo and enjoyed modest success. Many game developers were happy to make games for a competing system. In the mid-1990s, Sony introduced the PlayStation console,

which outsold Nintendo's N64. By the time the PlayStation 2 arrived, Sony had captured the majority of the video game market.

45   Video games today are, expectedly, far more complex than they were in 1972. The graphics on present systems make the blocky, basic-colored stick figures of early Atari games look like cave paintings. Coin-operated arcade games, once necessarily huge, now struggle with obsolescence because computer processors and high-resolution display screens are now no larger than postage stamps. In contrast
50   to the games of thirty years ago, each game today is a celebration of technology and a precursor of an increasingly digital future.

1. Early coin-operated video games were higher in quality than home systems because
    A. manufacturers directed more research funds to arcade games than home systems.
    B. the smaller, cheaper home systems did not contain large, expensive parts.
    C. advances in technology resulted in smaller components with greater capabilities.
    D. the inventor of *Pong* created coin-operated machines before home systems.
    E. consumers lost interest in the relatively lower quality of home systems.

2. A good substitute for the word *volatile* in line 22 would be
    A. insatiable.
    B. undetermined.
    C. unlikely.
    D. unpredictable.
    E. underestimated.

3. Which statement can be inferred from paragraph 4?
    A. Nintendo was preparing to corner the video game market.
    B. Video games were simply a fad.
    C. Atari overestimated the demand for game systems.
    D. Despite a lack of interest, consumers still wanted new games.
    E. Consumers preferred home systems to coin-operated games.

4. As used in line 37, *deplored* means the opposite of
    A. honored.
    B. identified.
    C. begged.
    D. condemned.
    E. reacted.

5. This passage is best described as
   A. prejudiced.
   B. science.
   C. backwards.
   D. persuasive.
   E. history.

Lesson Eight

1. **apathy** (ap´ ə thē) *n.* a lack of interest or emotion
    The teacher tried to overcome the general *apathy* among students in the ancient history class.
    syn: indifference; lassitude   *ant: concern; fascination*

2. **bludgeon** (bluj´ ən) *v.* to strike with a club
                                n. a short, heavy club with one end heavier than the other
    (v) He *bludgeoned* the swamp monster until it stopped moving.
    (n) The dinosaur used its spiked tail as a *bludgeon*.
    (v) *syn: beat; club*
    (n) *syn: cudgel; mace*

3. **cursory** (kûr´ sə rē) *adj.* performed quickly with little attention to detail
    Guards failed to notice the hole in the fence during a *cursory* patrol of the border.
    syn: hasty; perfunctory   *ant: thorough; meticulous*

4. **eloquent** (el´ ə kwənt) *adj.* clear, expressive, and moving in speech
    His *eloquent* voice can be heard on dozens of television advertisements.
    syn: articulate; fluent   *ant: inarticulate; awkward*

5. **forlorn** (fôr lôrn´) *adj.* wretched, hopeless, and pitiful
    The *forlorn* miners in the old photograph, covered with coal dust and bruises, did not appear capable of smiling.
    syn: miserable; unhappy   *ant: cheery; joyful*

6. **innumerable** (in nōō´ mer ə bəl) *adj.* too numerous to be counted
    Through the airplane window, the city below seemed to contain an *innumerable* number of buildings.
    syn: countless; immeasurable   *ant: few; little*

7. **murky** (mûr´ kē) *adj.* 1. dark and gloomy
                                2. cloudy; unclear
    (1) The youngest child was afraid to go into the *murky* cellar alone.
    (2) He decided not to go swimming when he saw the *murky* water of the lake.
    (1) *syn: dim; shadowy*   *ant: bright; illuminated*
    (2) *syn: obscured*   *ant: clear*

8. **ordeal** (ôr dēl´) *n.* a painful or difficult experience
Being mistaken for a wanted criminal was an *ordeal* he hoped would never happen again.
syn: trial; tribulation   *ant: cinch; cakewalk*

9. **phoenix** (fē´ niks) *n.* 1. a bird of Egyptian mythology that periodically burned itself up and then rose from the ashes with renewed youth and vigor   2. a person or thing of unmatched quality
   (1) Archeologists found depictions of a *phoenix* painted on the walls of the ancient tomb.
   (2) Because she is considered the *phoenix* of computer network security specialists, her services are booked solid for the next two years.
   (2) *syn: paragon; epitome*

10. **rebuff** (ri buf´) *v.* to refuse bluntly
                              n. a blunt refusal
   (v) She continually *rebuffed* his requests for a date.
   (n) He received a *rebuff* before he even finished voicing his request.
   (v) *syn: snub; slight*   *ant: accept; consent*
   (n) *syn: rejection; denial*   *ant: concurrence; acceptance*

11. **scrupulous** (skrōō´ pyə ləs) *adj.* 1. very attentive to what is right and wrong   2. extremely attentive to detail; meticulous
   (1) The *scrupulous* student easily could have kept the money she found, but instead turned it over to the rightful owner.
   (2) With *scrupulous* effort, the artist crafted the tiny, detailed, crystal figurines.
   (1) *syn: conscientious; principled*   *ant: immoral; unprincipled*
   (2) *syn: fastidious; painstaking*   *ant: careless; inattentive; negligent*

12. **specter** (spek´ tər) *n.* 1. a ghostly apparition
                              2. a mental image of an unsettling thing or event
   (1) She turned each corner of the haunted house with the expectation of seeing a frightening *specter*.
   (2) The *specter* of an erupting volcano destroying the village woke Felipe from his nightmare.
   (1) *syn: phantom; ghost; wraith*
   (2) *syn: vision*

13. **textile** (teks´ tīl **or** teks´ təl) *n.* cloth made from weaving or knitting
Most early *textiles* were made from cotton or wool.
syn: fabric; material

14. **ultimatum**   (ul tə mā´ təm)   *n.*   a final demand or threat
    In her *ultimatum*, she threatened to quit her job if her employer did not raise her salary.

15. **vanguard**   (van´ gärd)   *n.*   1. the forwardmost units of an advancing army
    2. any group leading a new trend in a certain field
    (1) The *vanguard* will weaken the enemy's defenses before the infantry advances.
    (2) The research division of the corporation is the *vanguard* of the robotics industry.
    (2) *syn: pioneer*

EXERCISE I – Words in Context

Using the vocabulary list for this lesson, supply the correct word to complete each sentence.

1.   He was a[n] _____ of integrity and could not be bribed.

2.   The kidnapping was a traumatic _____ for the child.

3.   When a poisonous snake crawled into the garage, Megan _____ it with a shovel.

4.   The _____ detective never thought of pocketing the cash he found during the drug bust.

5.   Though thirsty, the hiker refused to drink the _____ water from the pond.

6.   Residents have reported hearing _____ wails emanating from the supposedly haunted mansion on the hill.

7.   Haley bought some intricately decorated antique _____ and used them to make beautiful curtains.

8.   After the violent storm, workers performed a[n] _____ search for any fallen power lines along the road.

9. After the brief argument, she _____ his invitation to the party.

10. His _____ speech reached the hearts of many listeners.

11. Before commencing the attack on the city, Alexander issued the _____ to the enemy forces to surrender or be killed.

12. Sarah contemplated the _____ careers for which she will be prepared after graduation.

13. The science fiction novel, set in the future, evoked the _____ of an interplanetary war between humans and aliens.

14. Widespread _____ allowed the problem to grow until a solution seemed nearly impossible.

15. The prestigious university is a[n] _____ of technological advancement.

EXERCISE II – Sentence Completion

Complete the sentence in a way that shows you understand the meaning of the italicized vocabulary word.

1. In her biography, she describes the *ordeal* in which...

2. Students responded to the field trip idea with *apathy*, so the teacher decided...

3. The young executive was regarded as a *phoenix* of the growing industry until...

4. The voice on the phone was so *eloquent* that no one realized the caller was...

5. As a soldier in the king's *vanguard*, Simon worried...

6. The *forlorn* child told us...

7. The bank manager wanted *scrupulous* employees who...

8. Leo realized that the silent man was actually a *specter* when...

9. During the *cursory* check of the visitor's ID card, the guard failed to notice...

10. Janet remembered only a few of the *innumerable* faces she saw during...

11. Lexus *rebuffed* the promotion offer because...

12. According to the teacher's *ultimatum*, Doug will fail for the year if...

13. At the factory, machines produce *textiles* to be used for...

14. Unable to swim away fast enough, Tony *bludgeoned* the shark with his fist until...

15. To brighten the *murky* apartment, Lisa...

EXERCISE III – Prefixes and Suffixes

Study the entries and use them to complete the questions that follow.

The suffix –[et]ic means "characteristic of" or "pertaining to."
The suffix –ence means "state of" or "quality of."
The suffix –ly means "in the manner of" or "like."
The suffix –ness means "state," "quality," or "condition."

Use the provided prefixes and suffixes to change each root word so that it completes the sentence correctly. Then, keeping in mind that prefixes and suffixes sometimes change the part of speech, identify the part of speech of the new word by circling N for a noun, V for a verb, ADJ for an adjective, or ADV for an adverb.

1. (scrupulous) After printing false information that spawned riots, the publisher promised a higher degree of _____ from its editorial staff.

    N   V   ADJ   ADV

2. (cursory)   When Tim _____ checked the door lock at closing time, he failed to notice that a piece of tape was holding the bolt open.

    N   V   ADJ   ADV

3. (eloquent)   The _____ in her manner of speaking belied her shoddy appearance.

    N   V   ADJ   ADV

4. (apathy)   Barb's mood quickly turned _____ when she realized that the television show was nothing more than a lengthy advertisement for cookware.

    N   V   ADJ   ADV

EXERCISE IV – Critical Reading

The following reading passage contains vocabulary words from this lesson. Carefully read the passage and then choose the best answers for each of the questions that follow.

Roller coasters have filled a critical gap in the adventure arena since their inception in 1817. Thanks to these main attractions at amusement parks, any thrill-seeker who lacks access to personal jet aircraft, a bobsledding track, or skydiving equipment now, too, can enjoy the **specter** of rocketing to his or her screaming,
5 high-velocity demise—just for the price of admission. Parks are driven to build bigger, faster coasters as thrill-expectations increase, and currently, three of the largest roller coasters in the world stand more than 400 feet tall.

Constructed in 1997, *Superman: The Escape* at Six Flags Magic Mountain in California offers twenty-three seconds of driving force. Riders climb into a six-ton,
10 fifteen-passenger car. The car then accelerates along a straight track at a pace that few racecars can match, reaching 100 miles an hour in about seven seconds. Then the thrill really begins—the track turns skyward, shooting the car straight up the side of a 415-foot tower. Passengers brave enough to look around will notice that the track ends at the top of the tower; the car slows as it reaches the top, and then
15 plummets, *backwards*, down the tower, rendering riders weightless for almost seven seconds. The car once again reaches 100 miles an hour *in reverse* before slowing down, stopping, and allowing the blood flow to return to riders' heads. *Superman* was the first roller coaster to exceed 100 miles per hour; new coasters go faster, but, like the **innumerable** coasters that have set records in the past, it is
20 likely to provide excitement for years to come.

Those who **rebuff** coasters that do not have a continuous-loop track might visit Cedar Point, an Ohio park with a reputation for record-setting roller coasters. From the parking lot, visitors will see a red-and-yellow tower reaching toward the clouds. This 420-foot **phoenix** of roller coasters is the *Top Thrill Dragster*, and its
25 name is wholly appropriate. Riders board trains that look, fittingly, like top-fuel dragsters. They are then fired (propelled, actually) down a straight track as though out of a cannon. Riders are flattened in their seats as the train rockets to 120 miles an hour in *under four seconds*! Then, just as riders overcome the 4-g acceleration (a force equal to four-times one's own bodyweight), they abruptly ascend the vertical
30 tower. Unlike *Superman*, the track of *Top Thrill Dragster* does not stop at the top; it curves around, redirecting the train to shoot back down the other side. Some coaster fans claim that at the top, a **cursory** glance northward will allow riders to see Canada on the other side of Lake Erie. After rounding the top of the tower, the train nose-dives straight toward the ground, 400 feet below, giving the passengers
35 in the first car the ride of their lives, especially since the track features a 270-degree twist on the way down.

If *Top Thrill Dragster* fails to make you weak in the knees, at least for a few seconds, then perhaps you are destined to become an astronaut. Otherwise, you might try visiting Six Flags in New Jersey and taking a ride on *Kingda Ka*, the 456-
40 foot monster that advances the limits of the term "thrill ride." Built by the same company as *Top Thrill Dragster* and sharing a similar, continuous track layout,

Kingda Ka drives passengers to an intense 128 miles an hour in a heart-stopping 3.5 seconds. Even the fiercest rider will be devoid of **apathy** while being thrust up the side of a 456-foot tower, and if that fails to thrill, the twisting, head-first
45 plunge from 418 feet should make up for it. Be sure to bring a hat to cover up your prematurely aged white hair as you stagger off the ride.

Though each of the roller coasters is designed specifically to thrill and to push the human body to its limits, safety is the first concern of every park and coaster designer. *Superman, Top Thrill Dragster,* and *Kingda Ka* are the products of Intamin
50 AG, the **vanguard** of the roller-coaster industry credited with more than seventy coasters around the world. The vast engineering, testing, and **scrupulous** inspection that goes into each coaster drives its price into the tens of millions of dollars, but ensures that the thrill of a ride fits well within the physical limits of the ride's construction. The rides are inspected incessantly, and parks typically shut them
55 down if even the slightest problem is suspected.

Some may claim that a guarantee of safety detracts from the thrill, but such claims are silly; anyone who feels that screaming along in an open metal box at over 100 miles an hour hundreds of feet off the ground is boring should be checked for a pulse.

> Thanks to these main attractions at amusement parks, any thrill seeker who lacks access to personal jet aircraft, a bobsledding track, or skydiving equipment now, too, can enjoy the **specter** of rocketing to his or her screaming, high-velocity demise—just for the price of admission.

1. The tone of lines 2-5, shown above, is best described as
   A. serious.
   B. revealing.
   C. mournful.
   D. threatening.
   E. ironic.

2. According to the passage, *Superman: The Escape* differs from the other named roller coasters in that
   A. it exceeds 100 miles per hour.
   B. its track is not a continuous loop.
   C. it was constructed by the Specter Company.
   D. its tower is less than 400 feet tall.
   E. it has no theme.

3. As used in line 32, *cursory* most nearly means
   A. clever.
   B. thorough.
   C. hurried.
   D. talented.
   E. complete.

4. The word *astronaut* is used in line 39 because it is suggestive of
   A. people who must be able to endure harsh physical extremes.
   B. the towering height of the featured roller coasters.
   C. activities for people who enjoy being different.
   D. the technological advancement necessary to construct large rides.
   E. people who explore new worlds.

5. In line 43, *apathy* most nearly means the opposite of
   A. boredom.
   B. exception.
   C. ordeal.
   D. indifference.
   E. excitement.

Lesson Nine

1. **amass** (ə mas´) *v.* to gather things together, usually for pleasure or profit
    The successful fundraiser *amassed* more than enough money to pay for the class trip.
    syn: accrue; accumulate   *ant: distribute; dispense*

2. **bravado** (brə vä´ dō) *n.* a showy or false display of courage
    Behind Jimmy's *bravado* at the amusement park lay an intense fear of roller coasters.
    ant: modesty; humility

3. **commiserate** (kə miz´ ə rāt) *v.* to feel or to express sorrow; to sympathize
    People attending the funeral *commiserated* over the recent loss.
    ant: disdain

4. **deter** (di tûr´) *v.* to prevent from doing or happening
    The scarecrow *deters* crows from landing in the small cornfield.
    syn: daunt; prevent   *ant: encourage; support*

5. **euphemism** (yōō´ fə miz em) *n.* an inoffensive term substituted for an offensive term
    Some people use the phrase "at rest" as a *euphemism* for "dead."
    ant: dysphemism

6. **fledgling** (flej´ ling) *n.*   1. a young bird just ready to fly
                                          2. an inexperienced person
                            adj.   young and inexperienced
    (n.1) The mother bird pushed the *fledgling* out of the nest, forcing it to fly.
    (n.2) Tim is a *fledgling* to the game, so he often asks the veterans for advice.
    (a) The coach told the *fledgling* players that if they keep practicing, they will play in the next match.
    (n.2) *syn: neophyte; novice; tyro*   *ant: veteran; expert*
    (a)   *syn: callow; new*   *ant: experienced; mature*

7. **lavish** (lav´ ish) *adj.*   1. extravagant and abundant 2. excessively generous
                              v.   to give generously and extravagantly
    (a.1) Each chamber of the mansion was filled with *lavish* decoration.
    (a.2) Though she loved the *lavish* gift, she could not accept something so valuable.
    (v) Grandmother *lavished* attention on her two grandchildren.
    (a.1) *syn: opulent; sumptuous*   *ant: meager; scant*
    (a.2) *syn: bountiful; pampering*   *ant: stingy; cheap; costive*
    (v)   *syn: heap; bestow*   *ant: deprive; refuse*

8. **menagerie** (mə naj´ ə rē) *n.* a collection of animals on display
During the last day of the state fair, visitors could look at the *menagerie* of prize-winning horses and cattle.

9. **occult** (ə kult´) *adj.* of or dealing with magic or the supernatural
During the Salem Witch Trials of 1692, people were accused of engaging in *occult* activity.

10. **peripheral** (pə rif´ ər əl) *adj.* of, near, or related to the outer edge or boundary
The residents of the *peripheral* colonies simply want to be left alone.
syn: outermost; tangential   *ant: central; innermost*

11. **profusion** (prō fū´ zhən) *n.* a great quantity or amount; an abundance
The hurricane victims received a *profusion* of donated supplies.
syn: surfeit; plethora; surplus   *ant: dearth; scarcity; paucity*

12. **recluse** (rek´ lōōs) *n.* a person who lives a secluded, solitary life
Since the accident, Tim has been a *recluse* who neither leaves his cabin nor speaks to anyone.
syn: hermit   *ant: socialite*

13. **skittish** (skit´ ish) *adj.* nervously excitable
The *skittish* man trembled as he glanced quickly around the room, expecting the worst to happen.
syn: restive; edgy; restless   *ant: relaxed; calm*

14. **tangible** (tan´ jə bəl) *adj.* actual; real; capable of being perceived by the senses
The suspect might appear to be guilty, but he will be released unless the police find *tangible* evidence against him.
syn: concrete; palpable; substantial   *ant: intangible*

15. **undulate** (un´ jə lāt) *v.* to move in or cause to move in a wavelike motion
The gelatin sculpture *undulated* whenever someone bumped the table.
syn: ripple; roll

EXERCISE I – Words in Context

Using the vocabulary list for this lesson, supply the correct word to complete each sentence.

1. Crystal wanted to see _____ proof of the deal in the form of a written contract.

2. In order to maintain a mystical atmosphere, the fortuneteller decorated her room with _____ symbols.

3. "Pre-owned" is a[n] _____ often used in place of "used."

4. The sheets hanging on the clothesline _____ when the breeze stirs them.

5. The judge was arrested for having accepted _____ gifts in exchange for unfair rulings.

6. The surveillance cameras in the ceiling of the department store _____ shoplifters from stealing.

7. The factory stopped the assembly line after receiving a[n] _____ of complaints about the latest shipment of products.

8. The _____ who lives in the upstairs apartment orders all her groceries online so she never needs to leave the building.

9. His shaky hand and his refusal to look his opponent in the eye undermined his _____.

10. The _____ pilot had logged only ten hours of flight time.

11. A miniature _____ contains her entire collection of tiny glass animal figurines.

12. The king grew suspicious when poor citizens began to _____ great fortunes.

13. After the stroke, my grandmother lost her _____ vision and could see only what was directly in front of her.

14. Ever since he was struck by lightning, he has been _____ about walking outside during rainstorms.

15. The teammates _____ together during the long ride home after losing the big game.

EXERCISE II – Sentence Completion

Complete the sentence in a way that shows you understand the meaning of the italicized vocabulary word.

1. The gracious hosts *lavished* their guests with...

2. The teacher *commiserated* with the student's unwillingness to...

3. Ever since a wild pitch struck him in the head, the batter has been *skittish* about...

4. To make her scrapbook, Renee *amassed*...

5. Since Heidi has a *profusion* of tomatoes from her garden this year, she will...

6. The term "runner-up" is a *euphemism* that refers to...

7. In the film, a wizard uses *occult* forces to...

8. Without any *tangible* proof, the accusations are...

9. Jerome showed *bravado* during his first day on the job because...

10. A ring of wire fence *deterred* the rabbits from...

11. A *menagerie* at the zoo contained...

12. The stagnant water of the puddle *undulated* when...

13. Kevin's friends thought he had become a *recluse* because...

14. The *fledgling* skier was not yet ready to...

15. City dwellers fled to *peripheral* farms and villages of the kingdom when...

EXERCISE III – Prefixes and Suffixes

Study the entries and use them to complete the questions that follow.

The prefix *in–* means "in" or "not."
The suffix *–ent* means "performer of."
The suffix *–ion* means "act of," "state of," or "result of."
The suffix *–ive* means "tending to."

Use the provided prefixes and suffixes to change each root word so that it completes the sentence correctly. Then, keeping in mind that prefixes and suffixes sometimes change the part of speech, identify the part of speech of the new word by circling N for a noun, V for a verb, or ADJ for an adjective.

1. (recluse)   The _____ writer rarely makes public appearances.

    N   V   ADJ

2. (deter)   The city hoped that the new row of streetlights would be
    good _____ to burglars.

    N   V   ADJ

3. (commiserate) For weeks, every word of _____ she received
    reminded her of the tragic loss.

    N   V   ADJ

4. (tangible)   The cyclist had the best bicycle and clothing but lacked the
    _____ drive needed to win the race.

    N   V   ADJ

EXERCISE IV – Improving Paragraphs

Read the following passage and then answer the multiple-choice questions that follow. The questions will require you to make decisions regarding the revision of the reading selection.

(1) We all know how wonderful trees are, how they replenish the air, provide shade, and prevent erosion, among other things. (2) Now, just for a moment, forget about the environment and consider the greatest selfish use of a tree—no, not shade or furniture or firewood, but something far more personal than that: a living landmark. (3) Planting a tree is the ultimate way to leave your mark. (4) If you choose the right place to plant it, your tree might outlast nearby buildings or even entire villages. (5) During your lifetime—perhaps sixty years after you plant the seed—you can return to the spot with your great-grandchildren, look up at the **undulating** leaves of a towering maple, oak, beech, or elm, and say, "I planted this tree."

(6) Even a **fledgling** gardener can grow the mightiest tree. (7) First, identify the type of tree you want to grow. (8) For a hardy, fast-growing tree, choose a maple or an evergreen such as a spruce or pine. (9) Choose the finest specimen of the tree you can find, preferably in an area having a **profusion** of that particular species; you do not want a self-pollinating tree. (10) You might even select a tree that has some historical significance, or a tree that you remember from your childhood. (11) It will give your tree personal meaning or conversational value.

(12) Once you find the tree you like, **amass** seeds from it when they become dry enough to fall off the branches. (13) Clean the seeds by removing the wings; on maple seeds (the little "helicopters"), the wings are the thin portion extending from the body of the seed. (14) Elm, ash, pine, and birch have similar parts that should be removed. (15) Simply rub the seeds between your hands and allow the chaff to fall away. (16) Fruit seeds must be extracted from the fleshy fruit and then washed, though for certain reasons some fruit trees are not recommended.

(17) After you have finished cleaning the seeds as instructed, you must be successful in tricking the seeds and having made them believe that the season is wintertime. (18) This process is called *stratification*, and it allows the seeds to mature and prepare to *germinate,* or grow; note, however, that some species, such as trees whose seeds mature in the spring, or trees growing in tropical or warm climates, might not require this. (19) Some maples, for example, can be planted immediately. (20) If you are uncertain about your seeds, search the Internet for planting instructions specific to that species. (21) Mix the seeds into a slightly dampened peat moss mixture, put it in a plastic zipper bag, and refrigerate it for the next three to four months. (22) Ensure that the temperature is above freezing.

(23) The seeds will not grow if they are planted too deep, and they will dry out if they are too shallow. (24) After stratification, plant the seeds in moist topsoil. (25) The depth should be equal to the diameter of the seed. (26) Keep them at a steady room temperature. (27) As the seedlings grow, move them to larger pots. (28) Eventually, your tree, or trees, will be large enough to transplant to the chosen location, whether it is your backyard or perhaps a clearing in the forest. (29) As long as it receives enough sun and nutrients from the soil, the tree should flourish.

* Lesson Nine *

(30) **Deter** disappointment by starting with many seeds and planting more than one tree.

(31) Once your tree establishes itself and takes root, it will remain a **tangible** reminder of your effort, whether it is for you or for the children who swing from its branches one hundred years after you are gone. (32) Perhaps your tree will inspire a poem, or maybe two generals will meet there to sign a historic peace treaty. (33) Even if your tree does not become famous, or make you famous for planting it, at least it will be helping the Earth.

1. Including which subtopic would help to clarify paragraph 3?
    A. how fruit trees are more likely to be eaten by wildlife
    B. why fruit trees might not grow well
    C. the science behind stratification
    D. the limited uses of certain oak trees
    E. the life expectancy of evergreens

2. From the following choices, choose the most appropriate revision of sentence 17.
    A. Nextly, you must perform a process in which the seeds are in a simulated winter environment.
    B. Next, you must artificially trick the seeds into thinking that it is winter.
    C. Having chosen the seeds and collected them and cleaned them, they must think it is wintertime.
    D. Next, you must fool the seeds into believing that it is winter.
    E. The seeds you cleaned must feel the effects of a simulated winter snow.

3. Sentence 23 should be placed to follow
    A. sentence 20.
    B. sentence 22.
    C. sentence 25.
    D. sentence 27.
    E. sentence 29.

4. If this passage was written to convince people to plant trees, which choice best describes the author's strategy?
    A. to personify trees by using human characteristics to describe them
    B. to glorify the role of trees in the ecosystem
    C. to convince people that trees, too, have feelings
    D. to downplay the sentimental value of trees
    E. to give trees personal, rather than shared, significance

Review

Lessons 7 – 9

EXERCISE I – Inferences

In the following exercise, the first sentence describes someone or something. Infer information from the first sentence, and then choose the word from the Word Bank that best completes the second sentence.

Word Bank

volatile	forlorn	loquacious	incontrovertible
skittish	cursory	wanton	fledgling

1. Richard frowned and stared blankly, as though he had just lost his best friend.
   From this sentence, we can infer that Richard looks _____.

2. The scientist warned his assistant that the slightest bump could cause the unstable compound to explode.
   From this sentence, we can infer that the scientist is working with a[n] _____ substance.

3. It is nearly impossible to end a conversation with Jeff because he just keeps talking
   From this sentence, we can infer that Jeff is _____.

4. Christina leaped from her chair when she heard the doorbell ring.
   From this sentence, we can infer that Christina is _____.

5. The DNA test proved beyond a doubt that the suspect had been at the scene of the crime.
   From this sentence, we can infer that the DNA test was _____.

EXERCISE II – Related Words

Some of the vocabulary words from lessons 7–9 have related meanings. Complete the following sentences by choosing the word that best completes the specified relationship. Some word pairs will be antonyms, some will be synonyms, and some will be words often used in the same context.

1. *Urbane* is most synonymous with
   A. wanton.
   B. tangible.
   C. skittish.
   D. eloquent.
   E. volatile.

2. *Scrupulous* contrasts most with
   A. wanton.
   B. bravado.
   C. peripheral.
   D. loquacious.
   E. compatible.

3. Someone who *commiserates* is likely to be
   A. lavish.
   B. forlorn.
   C. eloquent.
   D. wanton.
   E. ornate.

4. *Phoenix* is nearly the opposite of
   A. specter.
   B. vanguard.
   C. occult.
   D. incontrovertible.
   E. fledgling.

5. Someone who is *fraught* with worries might also be
   A. cursory.
   B. loquacious.
   C. urbane.
   D. peripheral.
   E. skittish.

6. *Innumerable* might describe a[n]
    A. ordeal.
    B. profusion.
    C. euphemism.
    D. quip.
    E. arid.

7. A *loquacious* person might not enjoy the solitude of a[n]
    A. phoenix.
    B. specter.
    C. recluse.
    D. menagerie.
    E. quip.

8. *Amass* contrasts most with
    A. lavish.
    B. fraught.
    C. tantalize.
    D. undulate.
    E. microcosm.

9. The *petulant* student's attitude was not _____ with that of his lab
    partner.
    A. murky
    B. deplore
    C. volatile
    D. compatible
    E. skittish

10. A *volatile* situation can be a[n] _____ for someone who is not
    trained in such matters.
    A. euphemism
    B. menagerie
    C. petulant
    D. ordeal
    E. scoff

EXERCISE III – Crossword Puzzle

Use the clues to complete the crossword puzzle. The answers consist of vocabulary words from lessons 7 through 9.

Across

3. The diver accidentally kicked the sandy sea floor and caused the water to become _____.
6. Alone on the prairie, she heard the _____ wail of a distant coyote.
7. Few plants can survive on the _____ plains.
13. During the argument, Jim stumped his opponent by making a[n] _____ observation that could not be denied.
14. The successful broker _____[ed] enough wealth to buy her own island.
15. The _____ gentleman dressed well, never lost his patience in public, and always smiled as he listened to what others had to say.

Down

1. The board of directors _____[ed] at the employee's suggestion to decrease the number of hours in a workweek.
2. Once the _____ neighbor starts talking, it is difficult to get away.
4. According to mom's _____, the children could either stop complaining about the food or go to bed hungry.
5. The _____ artist looked forward to learning new techniques in class.
8. The vampire-hunter watched for signs of _____ activity as clues during the hunt.
9. A[n] _____ of mosquitoes last year caused most people to stay inside their homes.
10. The object he thought was a[n] _____ turned out to be nothing more than a curtain flapping in the breeze.
11. The boxer's _____ suddenly ceased when he saw the size of his challenger.
12. The barbarian horde _____[ed] the castle door with a battering ram.

EXERCISE III – Crossword Puzzle

Lesson Ten

1. **amendment** (ə mend´ mənt) *n.* an alteration or correction
An *amendment* to the history textbook covers events that took place after the original book was published.
syn: modification; revision

2. **calliope** (kə lī´ ə pē) *n.* an organ-like musical instrument having a keyboard that operates steam whistles
A *calliope* played as children stood in line to ride the carousel at the carnival.
syn: steam organ

3. **clairvoyance** (klâr voi´ əns) *n.* the power to see things that are invisible to the senses
The detective is so observant that some people construe his superior skills as *clairvoyance*.

4. **didactic** (dī dak´ tik) *adj.* intended to instruct or guide
A good children's book should be as enjoyable as it is *didactic*.
syn: educational; edifying

5. **epic** (ep´ ik) *adj.* impressive and magnificent; beyond ordinary
  n. a long, narrative poem detailing the deeds of a hero
   (a) World War II was an *epic* event that affected everyone on the planet to some degree.
   (n) In Homer's *epic*, "The Iliad," the Greek hero Achilles fights in the Trojan War.
   (a) *syn: classic*

6. **gruff** (gruf) *adj.* 1. stern and blunt in manner
  2. harsh-sounding; hoarse
   (1) The *gruff*, old sailor was not the most sociable person around, but he had a heart of gold.
   (2) Her *gruff* voice clearly indicated that she was not feeling well.
   (1) *syn: curt; brusque*   *ant: friendly; sociable*
   (2) *syn: rasping; gravely*   *ant: melodious*

7. **incomprehensible** (in kom pri hen´ sə bəl) *adj.* difficult or impossible to understand
Joe's willingness to give away his valuable possessions was *incomprehensible* to his greedy brother.
syn: inexplicable; perplexing   *ant: clear; understandable*

8. **lurch** (lûrch) *v.* 1. to move slowly and unsteadily
   2. to move suddenly
   (1) The zombies *lurched* toward the village and its sleeping inhabitants.
   (2) When the bus *lurched* forward, Kate spilled coffee on her lap.
   (1) *syn: stagger; stumble*   *ant: glide*
   (2) *syn: lunge; pitch*

9. **ocular** (ok´ yə lər) *adj.* of or relating to the eye or the sense of sight
   He sustained *ocular* damage when he tried to weld without wearing a
   welder's mask.
   syn: visual; optical

10. **palatable** (pal´ ə tə bəl) *adj.* 1. acceptable to the taste
    2. acceptable to the mind
    (1) The angry customer complained that his meal was not *palatable*.
    (2) The thought of spending a week in the wilderness was simply not
    palatable to her.
    (1) *syn: edible; tasty*   *ant: inedible; disgusting*
    (2) *syn: acceptable; satisfactory*   *ant: unacceptable; intolerable*

11. **quiver** (kwiv´ ər) *v.* to tremble rapidly
    n. 1. a shaky or trembling motion
    2. a case for holding arrows
    (v) He *quivered* when he saw what appeared to be a ghost.
    (n.1) The sight of the decomposing road kill gave her a *quiver*.
    (n.2) The archer filled his *quiver* with arrows before going on the hunt.
    (v) *syn: shudder; shiver; shake*
    (n.1) *syn: tremor; shudder*

12. **residual** (ri zij´ ōō əl) *adj.* left over, as after the end of a process
    The arthritis in his shoulder was a *residual* effect of an injury that
    occurred decades ago.
    syn: remaining; lingering

13. **stoic** (stō´ ik) *adj.* seemingly indifferent to pain, grief, or pleasure
    The defendant's story about the struggle leading up to her crime had little
    effect on the *stoic* judge.
    syn: stolid; impassive   *ant: emotional; passionate*

14. **tirade** (tī´ rād) *n.* a long, angry speech

    After simple mistakes caused the team to lose, the coach delivered a furious *tirade* in the locker room.

    syn: diatribe; rant; harangue; screed   *ant: panegyric; encomium*

15. **voracious** (vô rā´ shəs) *adj.* 1. eager to eat; greedily hungry
    2. having an insatiable appetite for a thing or activity

    (1) Each day, the *voracious* caterpillar will eat twenty times its body weight.

    (2) No matter where she went, the *voracious* reader always had a book in her hand.

    (1) *syn: ravenous; rapacious*   *ant: satiated; satisfied; sated*
    (2) *syn: avid*

EXERCISE I – Words in Context

Using the vocabulary list for this lesson, supply the correct word to complete each sentence.

1. Unable to contain his anger any longer, Caleb burst into a[n] _____ about inconsiderate neighbors who wake everyone in the middle of the night.

2. Many self-proclaimed psychics claim to have powers of _____ that allow them to see the future.

3. The yogurt has not yet reached its expiration date, so it should still be _____.

4. The university printed a[n] _____ that corrected an error in a previous handbook.

5. His _____ reply indicated that he did not feel like discussing the matter.

6. The _____ woman had been desensitized to emotional stress during her very difficult childhood.

7. The movie depicts the _____ journey of the first explorers to traverse the continent of Africa.

8. The _____ traveler devoured his meal as though he had not eaten for several days.

9. A brightly colored _____ provided music for the circus performers.

10. The secret language is _____ to anyone who does not know how to decode it.

11. If she had not been wearing sunglasses, the flying glass probably would have caused a[n] _____ injury.

12. When she sleepwalks, she _____ throughout the house in the middle of the night.

13. The _____ chemicals found during the police raid proved that the trailer had been used for the manufacture of illegal drugs.

14. The metal traffic sign _____ when it was struck by the draft of the speeding car.

15. Many children's cartoons are entertaining but lack any real _____ value.

EXERCISE II – Sentence Completion

Complete the sentence in a way that shows you understand the meaning of the italicized vocabulary word.

1. Jerry scheduled an *ocular* examination for himself because...

2. During a *didactic* visit to the museum, the children learned...

3. When the villagers heard the sound of a *calliope*, they...

4. The writer's tears had no effect on the *stoic* editor; he still believed...

5. Her legs asleep, Theresa stood up and then *lurched*...

6. Benjamin is a *voracious* adventurer who regularly...

7. The temperature rose to ninety-five degrees, so the workers were delighted with the boss's *palatable* suggestion to...

8. An *amendment* to the original document changed...

9. Behind every major city is an *epic* tale involving...

10. The arrogant genius claims his theory is *incomprehensible* to...

11. Through her gift of *clairvoyance*, she knew...

12. During his *tirade*, the teacher explained...

13. Jacob *quivered* when...

14. After watching the game, Emilio's voice was *gruff* because...

15. After making the main course, the chef used the *residual* ingredients to...

EXERCISE III – Prefixes and Suffixes

Study the entries and use them to complete the questions that follow.

The prefix *auto–* means "self" or "same."
The prefix *un–* means "not" or "opposite of."
The suffix *–ism* means "system" or "system of."
The suffix *–ity* means "state of" or "quality of."

Use the provided prefixes and suffixes to change each root word so that it completes the sentence correctly. Then, keeping in mind that prefixes and suffixes sometimes change the part of speech, identify the part of speech of the new word by circling N for a noun, V for a verb, or ADJ for an adjective.

1. (palatable) During the famine, people were forced to eat things that were normally considered _____.

    N   V   ADJ

2. (didactic) His _____ nature led him to teach himself to speak fluent French and Spanish without ever setting foot in a classroom.

    N   V   ADJ

3. (voracious) The teacher was surprised with the students' _____ for the subject.

    N   V   ADJ

4. (stoic) While her _____ protects her from deep emotional pain, it also restricts feelings of great joy.

    N   V   ADJ

EXERCISE IV – Critical Reading

The following reading passage contains vocabulary words from this lesson. Carefully read the passage and then choose the best answers for each of the questions that follow.

In the winter of 1941, a woman found herself running for her life through the Pyrenees Mountains between France and Spain—no small task for someone who just ten years before had lost her leg in a hunting accident. The Gestapo—the Nazi Secret Police—were searching for her. Who was this poor woman, and why did
5 Nazis want to kill her? Was she a refugee? A defiant villager?

Born in Baltimore in 1906, Virginia Hall had never planned to become one of the most dangerous allied agents in France. Throughout school, Hall's **didactic** studies gave her fluency in French, German, and Italian, and in 1931, Hall became a clerk at the American Embassy in Warsaw, Poland. She transferred to several
10 posts throughout Eastern Europe during the next eight years, finally ending up in Turkey, where she lost her lower leg during one of her adventurous outings. In 1939, the U.S. Department of State (DOS) denied Hall's request to become a Foreign Service Officer. The DOS cited her missing leg, but likely rejected Hall for her gender more than her injury. Insulted, Hall resigned her post and joined the
15 French Ambulance Service Unit, but the German invasion of France forced her to flee to England in 1940.

Hall returned to work as a clerk for the American Embassy in England, but she soon caught the attention of the British Special Operations Executive (SOE)—the agency directing the massive spy and sabotage operations in occupied Europe. After
20 some specialized weapons and communications training, she was ready for her first assignment.

Acting as a reporter for the New York Post, Hall deployed to France and set up resistance networks. She also helped to smuggle escaped prisoners of war and downed pilots to England. The war escalated in 1942, and Hall was forced to flee
25 once again as German troops flooded her area of operation—on foot through the Pyrenees Mountains.

During her few months away from France, Hall received more communications training and transferred to the American Office of Strategic Services (OSS), the forerunner to the Central Intelligence Agency (CIA). Not one to **quiver** in the
30 face of danger, Virginia, codenamed "Diane," returned to France in 1942. Disguised as a heavyset milkmaid, she directed supplies to French resistance, sabotaged German communications lines and military assets, and reported German military activity.

An unidentified "woman with a limp" thwarting operations was not a **palat-**
35 **able** situation to the Nazis, so the Gestapo searched for her constantly. Though her prosthetic leg was painful and caused her to **lurch**, Hall improved her cover by training herself to walk without limping.

By 1945, Virginia Hall had overseen the destruction of strategic bridges, German trains, and the capture of more than five hundred Nazi soldiers. She was
40 about to accept a new assignment to Austria, this time as "Camille," when the war ended.

When President Truman offered to present Hall with the Distinguished Service
Cross, a citation second only to the Medal of Honor, she politely declined, explaining that she intended to remain active as an intelligence agent. And she did; Hall
worked for the CIA from 1951 to 1966, quietly confronting threats to the nation
45 while the public slept at night. In 1982, Virginia died in Rockville, Maryland, a
little-known hero whose **voracious** craving for adventure was matched only by her
epic experiences.

1. As used in line 7, *didactic* most nearly means
   A. talented.
   B. language.
   C. learning.
   D. receiving.
   E. European.

2. Virginia Hall lost her leg in
   A. Turkey.
   B. the line of duty.
   C. occupied France.
   D. Baltimore.
   E. her third week of weapons training.

3. The word *palatable*, as used in line 34, means the opposite of the word
   A. meaningful.
   B. tasteful.
   C. agreeable.
   D. controversial.
   E. unacceptable.

4. According to the passage, Virginia never worked for which of the following
   organizations?
   A. Central Intelligence Agency
   B. National Security Agency
   C. Office of Strategic Services
   D. Department of State
   E. Special Operations Executive

5. All the following choices are major themes of the passage except
   A. women at war.
   B. the thankless work of secret agents.
   C. the psychological effects of war.
   D. discrimination in the workplace.
   E. dedication to a cause.

Lesson Eleven

1. **adversary** (ad´ vər sâr ē) *n.* an opponent or enemy
    Jordan's *adversary* will do anything to ensure that Jordan does not win the election.
    syn: foe; rival   *ant: fan; supporter*

2. **ambulatory** (am´ byōō lə tôr ē) *adj.* able to walk
    The *ambulatory* patient was led to an ambulance, but the other patient had to wait for a stretcher.

3. **cacophony** (kə kof´ ə nē) *n.* a harsh, unharmonious sound
    Heather woke to the *cacophony* of construction saws and hammers from the house next door.
    syn: clamor; discord   *ant: harmony*

4. **capricious** (kə prish´ əs) *adj.* subject to impulse, whim, or unpredictability
    She prefers her *capricious* style of grocery shopping to using a list.
    syn: fickle; whimsical; random   *ant: conventional; predictable*

5. **cumbersome** (kum´ bər səm) *adj.* difficult to handle, owing to weight or size
    The treasure hunter had no time to drag the *cumbersome* bags of gold out of the collapsing tomb.
    syn: unwieldy; bulky   *ant: compact; manageable*

6. **exacerbate** (ig zas´ ər bāt) *v.* to increase the severity of; to aggravate
    He *exacerbated* his leg injury by trying to walk off the field.
    syn: intensify; worsen   *ant: alleviate; improve*

7. **hierarchy** (hī´ ər är kē) *n.* a structure of rank, especially the highest positions
    The queen is currently the highest authority in the English *hierarchy*.
    syn: chain of command

8. **insatiable** (in sā´ shə bəl) *adj.* impossible to satisfy
    The young scientist had an *insatiable* hunger for knowledge.
    syn: voracious; ravenous   *ant: quenchable; satisfiable*

9. **meander** (mē an´ dər) *v.* to wander aimlessly; to follow a winding course
    The little creek *meanders* through the foothills of the Appalachian Mountains.
    syn: ramble; rove

10. **overt**   (ō vûrt´)   *adj.*   open and observable; not concealed or hidden
    She claimed to be happy despite her *overt* disappointment.
    syn: visible; evident   *ant: hidden; covert*

11. **piety**   (pī´ i tē)   *n.*   a state of devotion and reverence, especially to a
    supreme being or family
    The monks live in *piety* and seclusion at the mountain sanctuary.
    syn: faithfulness; holiness   *ant: impiety; inequity; malice*

12. **rebut**   (ri but´)   *v.*   to offer opposing arguments or evidence
    The defense attorney *rebutted* the witness's testimony.
    syn: refute   *ant: confirm; attest*

13. **squabble**   (skwob´ əl)   *v.*   to argue noisily over petty things
                                  n.   a noisy argument over a petty matter
    (v) The brother and sister *squabbled* over who should sit in the front seat.
    (n) Mom unplugged the television set in order to end Sal and Vera's
         senseless *squabble* over which program to watch.
    (v) *syn: quarrel; bicker*   *ant: agree; concur*

14. **treachery**   (trech´ ə rē)   *n.*   1. the intentional betrayal of trust
                                          2. a specific, intentional betrayal of trust
    (1) The commander reminded the soldiers that death was the punishment
         for *treachery*.
    (2) Many small *treacheries* among politicians contributed to the fall of the
         Roman Empire.
    (1) *syn: perfidy; treason*   *ant: loyalty; faithfulness; devotion*
    (2) *syn: disloyalty*

15. **validate**   (val´ i dāt)   *v.*   to confirm as official, legal, or legitimate
    A series of fatal accidents *validated* the need for a traffic light at the inter-
    section.
    syn: confirm; endorse; authorize

EXERCISE I – Words in Context

Using the vocabulary list for this lesson, supply the correct word to complete each sentence.

1. Catherine fills the highest position in the company hieracrchy

2. If Jason trains as well as his adversry on the opposing team, then he might win the next match.

3. Continued use of her sprained ankle exacerba the already painful injury.

4. Wes, a wanted criminal, accused his neighbors of treachry when the police arrived at his door.

5. A[n] cacophon of ear-piercing clangs emanated from the kitchen when the child started playing with the metal pots and pans.

6. Shannon did not agree with the author of a recent newspaper article, so she rebutted it in a letter to the editor.

7. The insaitable child was never happy to receive just one cookie.

8. The capricic child changed her mind every two minutes.

9. The roommates squabbled over which television show would be better to watch.

10. Garrett will be using crutches until he is ambulatory once again.

11. The ant meandered around on the kitchen floor until it found a single crumb.

12. She did not allow the police officer to enter her home until the station validated his identity.

13. The deliveryman had to stop to rest while carrying the cumbersom package up the stairs.

14. During the trial, the defendant's overt indifference to the law prompted the judge to recommend the maximum sentence.

15. The former nun's _piety_ was evident even though she left the convent long ago.

EXERCISE II – Sentence Completion

Complete the sentence in a way that shows you understand the meaning of the italicized vocabulary word.

1. Workers can climb the management *hierarchy* by…

   working hard

2. Such *treachery* was impossible to forgive because…

   they betrayed us

3. The queen knew that her *adversaries* would…

   try to kill her

4. The storeowner depends on *overt* video surveillance to…

5. A *cacophony* erupted in the alley when…

   two cats had a fight

6. Her *capricious* daily routine makes it difficult for anyone to…

   understand or find her

7. Jillian *meandered* aimlessly through life until…

   she found purpose

8. The service representative must *validate* the customer's credit card number before…

   using it to buy cars

9. Keeping the secret was *cumbersome* for Cody because…

   he was bad a keeping a

10. Only two of the four hikers were still *ambulatory* after…

    the mile long hike

11. They were good friends, but they always *squabbled* about…

    who got the last cookie

12. Alison *rebutted* the investigator's findings because…

    b/c she didn't want to go to jail

13. Brooke *exacerbated* the clutter in her bedroom when she…

    spilled her laundry basked

14. Heather's life of *piety* is apparent in the way in which she…

    is a nun

15. The *insatiable* restaurant customer refused…

    stop ordering

EXERCISE III – Prefixes and Suffixes

Study the entries and use them to complete the questions that follow.

The suffix –*al* means "pertaining to" or "characteristic of."
The suffix –*ate* means "to become" or "to cause to become."
The suffix –*ion* means "act of," "state of," or "result of."
The suffix –*ous* means "full of."

Use the provided prefixes and suffixes to change each root word so that it completes the sentence correctly. Then, keeping in mind that prefixes and suffixes sometimes change the part of speech, identify the part of speech of the new word by circling N for a noun, V for a verb, or ADJ for an adjective.

1. (insatiable) The restaurant's all-you-can-eat buffet is guaranteed to
    _____ even the hungriest customer.
    N   V   ADJ

2. (rebut)   During her _____, she asked her accuser what he was
    receiving for testifying against her.
    N   V   ADJ

3. (ambulatory) The charter bus stopped to allow the passengers some
    much-needed stretching and _____.
    N   V   ADJ

4. (cacophony) Fred's parents usually left the house to escape the
    _____ effect of his garage band's practicing.
    N   V   ADJ

EXERCISE IV – Critical Reading

The following reading passage contains vocabulary words from this lesson. Carefully read the passage and then choose the best answers for each of the questions that follow.

Just when we think we might know a little bit about the universe, observations tell us otherwise. New evidence suggests that the latest models of the universe are simply incorrect.

5   In the **hierarchy** of materials that makes up the universe, ordinary matter, the stuff that we can see, ranks low. Scientists estimate that normal matter, which makes up everything from tennis shoes to asteroid belts, constitutes a scant 5% of the universe. This seems like a pretty bold estimate when we look at some of the unimaginably large bodies in our own solar system alone, but scientists are fairly certain that there is more of what we don't see than what we do see.

10   Many millions of galaxies, each containing millions of stars, drift throughout our universe, and they all rotate. The speed at which the galaxies spin, however, is an **overt** sign that a new, undiscovered form of matter must exist. If galaxies were made up of merely normal matter, scientists contend, the stars would overcome the gravity of the system and hurtle outward. Something, some as-yet-undetected

15 matter, creates enough gravity to keep the galaxies intact as they spin. This matter, though still theoretical, is called *dark matter*, and it is estimated to make up 25% of the entire universe—five times more than the normal matter that composes you, me, and our planets and stars. Dark matter is also thought to be why galaxies appear in clustered arrangements throughout the universe. Certain strange objects

20 seem to **validate** the existence of dark matter; scientists have observed distortions in space caused by unseen forces, and invisible, X-ray-emitting clouds.

    A second observation further **exacerbates** the frustrations of scientists. The standard model of the universe, which abides the known laws of physics, no longer seems to apply. The rate at which the universe expands was once thought to be

25 slowing down; however, observations reveal the contrary: the expansion is speeding up as though some unknown force is driving everything away. If it is real—and, remember, we have known what electricity is for just a little more than a century— this *dark energy* comprises 70% of the universe.

    Plenty of scientists **rebut** the 5-25-70 theory because present technology is

30 too limited to make good observations. In addition, new observations suggest that clusters of galaxies are becoming more dense—the opposite of what should happen if dark energy is, indeed, acting against gravity. Cosmologists and astronomers will **squabble** over the truth for years to come; however, if the day of discovery should arrive, prepare for the life-altering advancements that accompanied the Ages of

35 Steel, Industry, and Communication. Determining the composition of the universe might take us to a new Age of Exploration—one in which we measure our voyages in the trillions of miles.

1. Dark matter is thought to exist because
    A. space is nothingness, but nothing is something.
    B. there is too much strange activity in the universe for it not to exist.
    C. there is not enough normal matter to cause the observed effects of gravity.
    D. dark energy cannot exist without dark matter.
    E. the planets rotate too quickly to be made completely of normal matter.

2. If you wanted the first sentence of paragraph 4 to have the opposite meaning, you should replace *exacerbates* with
    A. destroys.
    B. intimidates.
    C. frustrates.
    D. alleviates.
    E. comforts.

3. According to the passage, which choice makes up the largest part of the universe?
    A. dark matter
    B. X-ray-emitting clouds
    C. dark energy
    D. normal matter
    E. antimatter

4. As used in line 29, *rebut* most nearly means
    A. tolerate.
    B. allow.
    C. represent.
    D. recognize.
    E. deny.

5. The expression "day of discovery" in lines 33-34 refers to
    A. the time in which more is known about dark matter and dark energy.
    B. May 25ᵗ, 1970.
    C. a future day in which explorers perfect warp-speed space travel.
    D. the anniversary of the first moon landing.
    E. the day in which scientists first speculated that dark matter exists.

Lesson Twelve

1. **ajar** (ə jär´) *adj.* partially open
   The heater continued to run because someone left the door *ajar*.

2. **buffoon** (bə fōōn´) *n.* a clown, jester, or person who acts like one
   The ridiculous nature of his jokes led most people to think he was a *buffoon*.
   syn: fool; joker

3. **dexterous** (dek´ stər əs **or** dek´ strəs) *adj.* 1. skillful in physical movements, especially of the hands   2. having mental skills
   (1) The *dexterous* skipper could tie complicated knots in only seconds.
   (2) With experience, he became a *dexterous* politician.
   (1) *syn: adroit; nimble*   *ant: clumsy; inept*
   (2) *syn: clever*   *ant: foolish*

4. **engender** (en jen´ dər) *v.* to bring about; to give rise to
   The circular seating pattern of the classroom *engenders* class participation.
   syn: cause; produce   *ant: halt; stop*

5. **geology** (jē ol´ ə jē) *n.* 1. the scientific study of earth's structure and history   2. the natural structure of a specific region
   (1) She always had an interest in rock formations, so she studied *geology* in college.
   (2) Until more is known about the *geology* of the cave, no one should enter.

6. **impartial** (im pär´ shəl) *adj.* favoring neither side over the other; lacking favoritism
   The judge cannot be *impartial* in a case that involves her own daughter.
   syn: unbiased; neutral; disinterested   *ant: biased; predisposed*

7. **malicious** (mə lish´ əs) *adj.* wishing evil or harm upon others
   The airport security guards screen passengers for items that can be used for *malicious* purposes.
   syn: malevolent; hateful   *ant: benevolent; benign*

8. **nonchalant** (non shə länt´) *adj.* appearing casually unconcerned or indifferent
   In an effort to appear *nonchalant*, he faked a yawn.
   syn: blasé; detached   *ant: concerned; troubled*

9. **pantomime** (pan´ tə mīm) *v.* to communicate or tell a story using only facial expressions and bodily gestures; express without using words
He did not speak the language, so he *pantomimed* his question to the tour guide.
syn: mime

10. **prolific** (prō lif´ ik) *adj.* producing offspring or works in great abundance
Rex Stout, a *prolific* author, wrote more than seventy detective novels.
syn: productive; fruitful   *ant: barren; sterile*

11. **recede** (rē sēd´) *v.* to move back or away from a point or limit
The beach *recedes* each year because of erosion.
syn: withdraw; draw back   *ant: proceed; advance*

12. **sequester** (si kwes´ tər) *v.* 1. to put into seclusion or isolation; to keep away from others
2. to seize officially, sometimes forcibly
(1) She *sequestered* herself in her bedroom to study for the final exam.
(2) The police *sequestered* the vendor's entire inventory when it was found to contain many stolen items.
(1) *syn: segregate; isolate*   *ant: assimilate; integrate*
(2) *syn: confiscate; appropriate*   *ant: restore; return*

13. **tawdry** (tô´ drē) *adj.* cheap and gaudy; showy; sleazy
His *tawdry* suit looked more like the upholstery of a cheap sofa.
syn: tacky; garish; cheesy   *ant: elegant; stylish; classy*

14. **uncouth** (un kōōth´) *adj.* not refined; crude or ungraceful
Eric's *uncouth* behavior at the upscale restaurant embarrassed Linda.
syn: coarse; uncivil; vulgar   *ant: polite; genteel; urbane*

15. **vulnerable** (vul´ nər ə bəl) *adj.* susceptible to injury, attack, or persuasion
His weakened immune system made him *vulnerable* to infection.
syn: defenseless; susceptible; at risk   *ant: impervious; invincible*

EXERCISE I – Words in Context

Using the vocabulary list for this lesson, supply the correct word to complete each sentence.

1. She _____ her message because no one could hear her through the soundproof windows.

2. The ice cream melted because someone left the freezer door _____.

3. The baby sea turtles are _____ to predators as they make their way from the beach to the ocean.

4. Patrick's _____ answer revealed his general lack of interest in the subject.

5. She sometimes acts like a[n] _____ to get a laugh out of her class-mates.

6. The teacher sent a note to Jimmy's parents because of his _____ behavior during the speaker's presentation.

7. The _____ man played complicated piano music with little effort.

8. Dozens of popular magazines display the _____ artist's work.

9. The _____ clothes were too outlandish to wear in public, but fine for wearing while painting.

10. The _____ of San Francisco makes the city very susceptible to earthquakes.

11. The detective _____ each of the two suspects so they could not cor-roborate their alibis.

12. Neither greed nor revenge motivated the crime; it was purely a[n] _____ act meant to harm innocent people.

13. The referee made _____ calls that never seemed to favor a specific team.

14. They plan to wait until the crowd **recede** before getting in line to buy lunch at the concession stand.

15. The overuse of antibiotics _engender_ new strains of drug-resistant germs.

EXERCISE II – Sentence Completion

Complete the sentence in a way that shows you understand the meaning of the italicized vocabulary word.

1. The scientists called an expert in *geology* to determine…

2. She left the door *ajar* because… she was afraid of the dark

3. The water line of the river *recedes* when… the tide goes out

4. Dana felt that the new television show for younger viewers was *malicious* because… it topic included gory

5. The *uncouth* dinner guest surprised everyone when…

6. The *prolific* composer wrote… thousands of pieces

7. Teri wanted to buy the car, but she acted *nonchalant* when the salesman approached because… she wanted a good discount

8. The warm, damp conditions in the basement *engender*…ed the spookiness of downstand

9. A person who is *vulnerable* to suggestion might… speak a-lot

10. The *dexterous* child was very good at…

11. Because they were underwater, the divers *pantomimed*… their reaction to a shark

12. Soldiers *sequestered* the rebels who…

13. Hayden tried to write an *impartial* critique of the film, but it was difficult because…

14. The prince donned *tawdry* clothing in order to…

15. Everyone expected the *buffoon* to…

EXERCISE III – Prefixes and Suffixes

Study the entries and use them to complete the questions that follow.

The prefix *inter–* means "between" or "among."
The suffix *–ery* means "the act of" or "the practice of."
The suffix *–ist* means "doer of" or "follower of."
The suffix *–ity* means "state of" or "quality of."

Use the provided prefixes and suffixes to change each root word so that it completes the sentence correctly. Then, keeping in mind that prefixes and suffixes sometimes change the part of speech, identify the part of speech of the new word by circling N for a noun, V for a verb, or ADJ for an adjective.

1. (dexterous) The juggler's natural _____dexterity_____ allowed him to juggle five items simultaneously.

    <u>N</u> V ADJ

2. (buffoon) Mike received an after-school detention when his _____ caused a disruption during class.

    N V ADJ

3. (recede) When the argument between her daughters escalated, Teri decided to _____ by sitting and listening to both sides of the situation. *Intercede*

    N <u>V</u> ADJ

4. (geology) The _____geologists_____ warned citizens that their homes were built directly above a major fault line.

    <u>N</u> V ADJ

EXERCISE IV – Improving Paragraphs

Read the following passage and then answer the multiple-choice questions that follow. The questions will require you to make decisions regarding the revision of the reading selection.

(1) Although CBS and the Game Show Network call it a "scandal," the only scandalous aspects of Michael Larsen's winning more than $110,000 in cash and prizes on the popular game show *Press Your Luck* were how CBS left itself **vulnerable** to a strategy like Larsen's and how Larsen himself squandered his winnings and died a bankrupt fugitive.

(2) Larsen, a broke and unemployed ice-cream truck driver, watched a lot of *Press Your Luck* during the long winters in Ohio. (3) In the north, ice-cream is not in big demand during the winter months. (4) When he figured out that the "random" placement of prizes, free spins, and whammies under the squares on the "Big Board" was not random at all, he taught himself how to select a square that would award him both cash and a free spin at every turn. (5) With that knowledge, Larsen spent his last $100 on a ticket to Los Angeles and tried out to be a contestant on the show.

(6) He had no **malicious** intent. (7) He was not out to commit fraud. (8) He simply wanted to win some big cash—fast. (9) And he did. (10) After a disastrous first round in which he actually selected a whammy (some say he had not yet grown **dexterous** in handling the plunger that selected the squares), he completed forty-five consecutive spins and amassed winnings of $110,237 in cash, plus a few fabulous vacations.

(11) Once producers of the show realized what Larsen had done, they tried to block awarding him his prizes, saying he essentially cheated, but an **impartial** judgement awarded Larsen everything. (12) The judge faulted CBS because its Big Board's sequences were based on flawed programming.

(13) For his part, Larsen lost nearly half of his winnings in a dubious real estate deal back in Ohio. (14) He lost the rest of his money, too. (15) He withdrew $50,000 in one-dollar bills from his bank account in order to find two bills with consecutive serial numbers and win a local radio station's $30,000 prize. (16) After he and his girlfriend **sequestered** themselves in his house for several days, they left for a few hours to attend a Christmas party. (17) While they were gone, a burglar stole the full remainder of his *Press Your Luck* winnings.

(18) Soon, Larsen found himself wanted by the FBI and the Securities and Exchange Commission for questioning about his involvement in the dubious real estate deal that had cost him the first half of his winnings, and he went on the run. (19) He died a few years later, broke and hiding in Florida.

(20) This event is referred to as the "Press Your Luck Scandal," but there really was no scandal. (21) No one cheated. (22) No one violated any laws. (23) But an overconfident television network was caught not really safeguarding its own best interests, and a clever gameplayer allowed his own greed and carelessness to deprive him of the comfortable life his winnings could have bought him.

1. Which unnecessary sentence(s) in paragraph 2 should be deleted?
   A. sentence 2
   B. sentence 3
   C. sentence 4
   D. sentence 5
   E. sentences 3 and 5

2. Choose the revision that best improves paragraph 3.
   A. Combine sentences 6 and 7.
   B. Replace "plus" with "in addition to" (sentence 10).
   C. Delete sentence 8.
   D. Insert a comma after "round" in sentence 10.
   E. Use Larsen's name at least once.

3. If the author wanted to combine sentences 14 and 15, which choice would be the most logical way?
   A. He lost the rest of his money, too; by withdrawing $50,000...
   B. He lost the rest of his money as a withdrawal of $50,000...
   C. He lost the rest of his money when he withdrew $50,000...
   D. He lost the rest of his winnings of money, also, because he withdrew $50,000...
   E. He lost the money when he withdrew $50,000...

4. From the following sentences, choose the most appropriate one to end the concluding paragraph.
   A. It just goes to show, easy come, easy go.
   B. And that is the real scandal.
   C. "Don't put all your eggs in one basket" is the moral of this story.
   D. Therefore, this should be referred to as the "Press Your Luck Event."
   E. A sad, sad tale, indeed.

Review

Lessons 10 – 12

EXERCISE I – Inferences

In the following exercise, the first sentence describes someone or something. Infer information from the first sentence, and then choose the word from the Word Bank that best completes the second sentence.

Word Bank

uncouth	ocular	cumbersome	residual
stoic	capricious	gruff	epic

1. Marshall's facial expression did not change even when he learned that he had just won the lottery.
   From this sentence, we can infer that Marshall is _____.

2. The injury rendered Leah sightless for the rest of her life.
   From this sentence, we can infer that Leah sustained a[n] _____ injury.

3. The rude guest gnawed on a roasted turkey leg, chewed with his mouth open, and then used the tablecloth to wipe his face.
   From this sentence, we can infer that the guest is _____.

4. After the seawater boiled away, salt crystals lay on the bottom of the pan.
   From this sentence, we can infer that the salt is _____.

5. Tim struggled to carry the heavy sack of potatoes up the stairs, occasionally losing his grip.
   From this sentence, we can infer that the sack is _____.

EXERCISE II – Related Words

Some of the vocabulary words from lessons 10–12 have related meanings. Complete the following sentences by choosing the word that best completes the specified relationship. Some word pairs will be antonyms, some will be synonyms, and some will be words often used in the same context.

1. The *stoic* doctor cannot allow himself to be emotionally _____ to the suffering of his patients.
   A. ocular
   B. palatable
   C. vulnerable
   D. residual
   E. tawdry

2. The accident victim was *ambulatory* enough to _____ to the side of the road.
   A. lurch
   B. sequester
   C. quiver
   D. rebut
   E. pantomime

3. The *uncouth* wedding guest intentionally wore _____ clothing that would cause a distraction.
   A. palatable
   B. dexterous
   C. vulnerable
   D. didactic
   E. tawdry

4. The *treachery* was not accidental, but a[n] _____ act of greed.
   A. epic
   B. malicious
   C. capricious
   D. prolific
   E. gruff

5. *Validate* means the opposite of
   A. tirade.
   B. rebut.
   C. recede.
   D. engender.
   E. treachery.

6. *Overt* contrasts most with
    A. clairvoyance.
    B. voracious.
    C. ajar.
    D. incomprehensible.
    E. nonchalant.

7. *Voracious* is synonymous with
    A. incomprehensible.
    B. cumbersome.
    C. insatiable.
    D. malicious.
    E. tawdry.

8. A *gruff* person would have difficulty sounding
    A. nonchalant.
    B. uncouth.
    C. incomprehensible.
    D. cacophony.
    E. malicious.

9. In meaning, *exacerbate* contrasts most with
    A. quiver.
    B. squabble.
    C. pantomime.
    D. engender.
    E. recede.

10. A *capricious* person might be content to _____ all day long.
    A. lurch
    B. rebut
    C. meander
    D. validate
    E. squabble

EXERCISE III – Crossword Puzzle

Use the clues to complete the crossword puzzle. The answers consist of vocabulary words from lessons 10 through 12.

Across

1. Each year, the _____ tree produced thousands of peaches.
4. Mr. Roberts burst into a[n] _____ about lousy drivers when some-one ran a red light at the intersection.
5. Since the bank was closed, the police officer knew that the person in the window was there for some _____ reason.
6. The court _____[ed] members of the jury so they could not be influenced during the trial.
8. The bright sunlight further _____[d] her headache.
11. Standing water _____[s] swarms of mosquitoes that hatch from eggs laid in it.
13. After the failed campaign, the politician had to refund any _____ campaign contributions.
14. The patrolman would not have given the driver a ticket if it were not for her _____ disregard for safety.

Down

2. The foreign language was _____ to the traveler.
3. Alicia was playing to win, but so was her _____.
6. While Ben _____[d] with the shopkeeper about the price of the item, another customer took the last one, leaving Ben with none.
7. Her pet turtle _____[s] in the back yard, constantly seeking shade and tasty morsels of fruit.
9. The _____ clarifies a confusing sentence in the original document.
10 The cast of the play wears _____ costumes that help draw attention to the action.
12 The _____ war consumed the lives and culture of five consecutive generations.

EXERCISE III – Crossword Puzzle

Lesson Thirteen

1. **acquiesce** (ak wē es´) *v.* to agree or comply reluctantly but without protest
   Laura did not want to go to the theme park for the family vacation, but she *acquiesced* to her children's wishes.
   syn: yield; concede; defer   *ant: defy; resist*

2. **cite** (sīt) *v.*   1. to refer to or quote as support or example
                          2. to praise officially; to honor
                          3. to summon before a court
   (1) The attorney *cited* an obscure law in defending his client's criminal actions.
   (2) The commander *cited* her with a medal for meritorious service.
   (3) The police officer *cited* the driver for having run through a red light.
   (1) *syn: mention; advert*
   (2) *syn: commend; acclaim; extol*

3. **cynical** (sin´ i kəl) *adj.* skeptical or pessimistic toward the motives of others
   The *cynical* patient believes that doctors will find something to diagnose even if she is in perfect health.
   syn: unbelieving; sardonic   *ant: trusting; optimistic*

4. **denote** (di nōt´) *v.* to indicate; to signify directly
   On the roadmap, little tents *denote* campgrounds.
   syn: represent; mean   *ant: connote*

5. **dismantle** (dis man´ tl) *v.* to take apart; to disassemble
   Mark *dismantled* the swing set because several children had hurt themselves while playing on it.
   syn: deconstruct   *ant: assemble; build*

6. **extortion** (ik stôr´ shən) *n.* the act of obtaining through force, intimidation, or abuse of authority
   The new district attorney promised to put a stop to bribery and *extortion* among corrupt officials.

7. **indignant** (in dig´ nənt) *adj.* very angry
   Neil becomes *indignant* when the neighbor's noisy dog keeps him awake all night.
   syn: incensed   *ant: relaxed; serene*

8. **luscious** (lush´ əs) *adj.* rich and appealing to the senses
The hungry, lost hiker nearly fainted when he saw the tree loaded with *luscious* pears.
syn: scrumptious; delicious　　　　　*ant: unappetizing; disgusting*

9. **oppressive** (ə pres´ iv) *adj.* 1. enforcing excessive power and control
　　　　　　　　　　　　　　　2. difficult to endure; burdensome
(1) People who criticized the *oppressive* government were known to disappear without a trace.
(2) The farmer struggled to push the plow in the *oppressive* heat.
(1) *syn: tyrannical; domineering*　　　　　*ant: permissive; tolerant*
(2) *syn: arduous; demanding*　　　　　*ant: easy; effortless; painless*

10. **ponderous** (pon´ dər əs) *adj.* 1. very heavy; unwieldy because of weight
　　　　　　　　　　　　　　　2. dull and labored
(1) The *ponderous* stones are nearly impossible for one person to stack without help.
(2) After a *ponderous* search, she found the earring she had lost in the backyard.
(1) *syn: cumbersome; weighty; bulky*　　　　*ant: light; weightless*
(2) *syn: laborious; wearisome*　　　　*ant: interesting; enjoyable*

11. **requisition** (rek wi zish´ ən) *n.* a formal request or demand
　　　　　　　　　　　　　　　v. to request officially
(n) Company headquarters rejected his *requisition* for new vehicles.
(v) She *requisitioned* a new computer when her old one became obsolete.

12. **suffrage** (suf´ rij) *n.* the right to vote
The nineteenth amendment guarantees women's *suffrage*.

13. **unbridled** (ūn brīd´ ld) *adj.* unrestrained; wild
When they learned that they were going to the theme park, the children reacted with *unbridled* enthusiasm.
syn: uncontrolled; uninhibited; rampant　　　　*ant: limited; restrained*

14. **utopia** (ū tō´ pē ə) *n.* a perfect society, especially socially or morally
The experimental *utopia* failed because there were no perfect people to live in it.
　　　　　　　　　　　　　　　ant: dystopia

15. **virtuoso** (vûr chōō ō´ sō) *n.* a musician having superior skill
The *virtuoso* played a complex solo that left the audience in awe.
syn: maestro

EXERCISE I – Words in Context

Using the vocabulary list for this lesson, supply the correct word to complete each sentence.

1. The candidate gained the support of the starving masses by promising to build a[n] _____ in which no one goes hungry.

2. Through _____, the mobsters forced all local business owners to pay a monthly fee for operating in the neighborhood.

3. The _____ man always assumes that politicians are considering only their own personal interests.

4. Because they felt they were mature enough, the seventeen-year-olds in the senior class petitioned for _____ in the upcoming election.

5. On the program for the graduation ceremony, an asterisk next to a name _____ that the student graduated with honors.

6. Miguel's _____ workload keeps him working well into the evening, but he makes double the wages for each hour of overtime.

7. The famous cello _____ began playing when she was only four years old.

8. Chelsea _____ to the committee's decision when she realized that no one else liked her idea.

9. Doug regretted his decision to go on a diet when he saw his wife eating a[n] _____ hot-fudge sundae.

10. He was known to steal candy from children during fits of _____ greed.

11. To comply with the nuclear nonproliferation treaty, the two nations _____ most of their nuclear weapons.

12. All _____ for the new office equipment were cancelled until next year due to budget restraints.

13. Sean was _____ when he saw that someone had dented his new car and then fled the parking lot.

14. In his term paper, Nathan _____ several experts on the subject.

15. After the professor's _____ lecture on the first day of class, no one was excited about returning.

EXERCISE II – Sentence Completion

Complete the sentence in a way that shows you understand the meaning of the italicized vocabulary word.

1. Lenny was arrested for *extortion* when an accountant noticed…

2. The checkmark on the top of the assignment *denotes*…

3. Holly *acquiesced* when her boss asked…

4. The *cynical* woman refused to give money to the homeless man because…

5. In an *unbridled* display of jealousy, George…

6. At the end of the state fair, workers *dismantled*…

7. The *virtuoso* draws crowds of fans who…

8. Only dues-paying members of the organization are granted *suffrage* when…

9. The *oppressive* heat forced many residents to…

10. The *ponderous* package was nearly impossible to…

11. Unlike the *luscious* food shown during the television commercial, the actual food at the restaurant looked…

12. The new manager's first *requisition* was…

13. He *cited* the recent string of burglaries as a reason for…

14. It is impossible to build a *utopia* on Earth because…

15. Preston's parents grew *indignant* when…

EXERCISE III – Prefixes and Suffixes

Study the entries and use them to complete the questions that follow.

The suffix –*ation* means "act of" or "result of."
The suffix –*ence* means "state of" or "quality of."
The suffix –*ism* means "system" or "system of."
The suffix –*ist* means "doer of" or "follower of."

Use the provided prefixes and suffixes to change each root word so that it completes the sentence correctly. Then, keeping in mind that prefixes and suffixes sometimes change the part of speech, identify the part of speech of the new word by circling N for a noun, V for a verb, or ADJ for an adjective.

1. (cite) Melanie received a[n] _____ for rescuing the child from the burning building.

    N   V   ADJ

2. (suffrage) She was the first _____ to demand equal voting rights for women.

    N   V   ADJ

3. (acquiesce) He did not like the idea, but gave his _____ by failing to say "no."

    N   V   ADJ

4. (cynical) The latest scandal in the company seemed to justify the _____ of employees.

    N   V   ADJ

EXERCISE IV – Critical Reading

The following reading passage contains vocabulary words from this lesson. Carefully read the passage and then choose the best answers for each of the questions that follow.

It's always fun to **dismantle** old books and movies set in the future and point out the details that simply never came to be; for example, the nylon jumpsuits, legions of robot servants, and nuclear hover-cars that were expected of humans in the year 2000 by humans of the 1950s. We know that the technological **utopias**
5 never emerged, but we should not be too **cynical** about the high hopes of past generations; their dreams, after all, inspired many of the technologies that we do enjoy today. In addition, we are likely guilty of the same silly assumptions; consider flashlights, for instance.

We would laugh if we saw characters in a modern television show using oil
10 lamps as light sources, but we do not think twice when we see space explorers, set three centuries into the future, using flashlights available at our local hardware stores of the present. Why pick on something as practical as flashlights? Because, thanks to night vision technology, the trusty flashlight might soon join the torch and the candle as it **acquiesces** to the next generation of tools used for seeing in
15 the dark: night vision goggles.

First developed for snipers during World War II, night vision has quietly advanced throughout six decades of use. The first devices were **ponderous** units that required heavy, external battery packs which were **oppressive** to carry around. Since then, the main type of night vision device has become very small and light-
20 weight by comparison, but its principle of operation has remained the same.

The moon and stars illuminate things at night just as the sun does during the day, but our eyes are not sensitive enough to see the reflected light. The starlight scope (SLS) allows a user to see in the dark by intensifying any available light. At a glance, a modern SLS might look like a small telescope, a monocular, or, if
25 doubled-up, a set of binoculars. Photons of light enter the lens and strike an intensifying screen. Each photon of light basically knocks an electron off the other side of the screen. The electrons fly down an intensifying tube toward the user (the tube might be no more than a few inches long). During their flight, the electrons pass through material that increases their numbers before they hit the next screen—the
30 phosphor screen. The phosphor screen is very similar to the screen of an old television set; each tiny phosphor glows when an electron strikes it, some brighter than others, depending on the number of electrons. Millions of tiny phosphors glow different shades, and the result is a picture of whatever the user is looking at, but illuminated as though it were daytime. This picture is what the user sees. Typically,
35 the phosphor screen is green because the human eye can detect more shades of green than any other color.

A starlight scope does have a drawback: it will not work in total darkness. To correct this, designers simply add a unique type of flashlight to the night vision device that projects infrared (IR) light, which is invisible to the human eye. The
40 user simply turns on the IR light and "illuminates" the area. The IR light reflects off objects in the field of view and enters the night vision goggles (NVGs). An infrared

imager in the goggles then converts the IR signals into visible light, which allows the user to see. Most modern NVGs have both SLS and IR capability.

45 Since a good set of NVGs currently costs thousands of dollars, night vision devices are not likely to replace flashlights overnight; however, to compare technology, the price of a desktop computer dropped from $3000 to $300 in fewer than ten years, and modern, handheld PDAs have more processing power than the best computers of the last decade. Is it so outrageous to think that in twenty years from today, people might surrender their flashlights to **requisition** a new pair of night

50 vision sunglasses, or night vision windows for their automobiles? If advancement in computer technology **denotes** the speed at which night vision will progress, it seems quite possible; granted, it is still not a legion of robot servants, but perhaps they will follow.

1. As it is used in line 17, *ponderous* is most nearly the opposite of
   A. delicate.
   B. cumbersome.
   C. thoughtful.
   D. bulky.
   E. dynamic.

2. According to paragraph 4, a starlight scope (SLS) forms a picture by converting
   A. phosphors to photons, and then photons to green electrons.
   B. visible light into a display screen.
   C. available light into high-speed, infrared light photons from the user's area.
   D. photons into electrons, and electrons into visible light on a screen.
   E. the green phosphors into invisible projections of infrared light.

3. Someone using night vision goggles is likely to see everything in green because
   A. infrared light appears green after passing through an intensifier.
   B. night vision devices detect only green light.
   C. people are most sensitive to differences in green light.
   D. night vision goggles are usually used in jungle environments.
   E. green light does not strain the human eye.

4. The best substitute for *denotes* as it is used in line 51 is
   A. explains.
   B. signifies.
   C. conducts.
   D. guesses.
   E. involves.

5. The author of the passage would agree with which of the following statements?
   A. Robot servants will precede night vision.
   B. Flashlights will never become obsolete.
   C. Too many advancements are throwing civilization into panic.
   D. Few people successfully predict how the future will look.
   E. Writers of the past made more accurate predictions of the future than writers of the present.

Lesson Fourteen

1. **abstinence** (ab´ stə nəns) *n.* the practice of refraining from indulgence; doing without
   Members of the vegetarian club practiced *abstinence* from meat.
   syn: self-denial   *ant: indulgence*

2. **annihilation** (ə nī ə lā´ shən) *n.* total destruction
   A deadly plague caused the *annihilation* of the entire herd of livestock.
   syn: obliteration   *ant: defense; protection*

3. **callous** (kal´ əs) *adj.* emotionally unfeeling; insensitive
   She became *callous* after enduring so many years of suffering.
   syn: heartless; impassive   *ant: sensitive; compassionate*

4. **delve** (delv) *v.* to search deeply, as though digging
   The company *delved* into the applicant's work history before hiring him for the classified position.
   syn: investigate; probe   *ant: gloss over; skim*

5. **entrails** (en´ trālz) *n.* the internal organs, especially intestines
   When the biology class dissected frogs, Pam became pale after seeing her frog's *entrails*.
   syn: guts; viscera

6. **grapple** (grap´ əl) *v.* to wrestle fiercely *n.* a metal shaft having multiple hooks, often thrown with a rope for climbing, and used for grasping and holding an object
   (v) He *grappled* with the idea for two days before finally making a decision.
   (n) The pirates threw a *grapple* onto the merchant ship and pulled it closer to their own vessel.
   (v) *syn: fight*
   (n) *syn: grapnel*

7. **incipient** (in sip´ ē ənt) *adj.* beginning to exist or become noticeable; in an early stage of development
   The nervous king planned an escape when he saw the signs of an *incipient* uprising.
   syn: developing   *ant: full-blown*

8. **mandatory** (man´ də tôr ē) *adj.* required; obligatory
   In some states, wearing a helmet while riding a motorcycle is *mandatory*.
   syn: compulsory   *ant: voluntary; optional*

9. **obliterate** (ə blit´ ə rāt) *v.* to destroy entirely; to wipe out completely
Using a wrecking ball and a bulldozer, the demolition crew *obliterated* the row of condemned buildings.
syn: eradicate; annihilate   *ant: preserve; create*

10. **pliable** (plī´ ə bəl) *adj.* easily shaped or bent, in form or in mind
He formed a crude funnel out of the *pliable* sheet of tin.
syn: flexible; pliant   *ant: rigid; inflexible*

11. **rummage** (rum´ ij) *v.* to search thoroughly and hastily, often chaotically
He *rummaged* through his pockets, desperately hoping to find his missing wallet.
syn: delve; fumble; grope

12. **solemn** (sol´ əm) *adj.* 1. serious and sincere
 2. revered sincerely and seriously
 (1) Her *solemn* expression showed that she found nothing funny about the joke.
 (2) Each year, they have a *solemn* feast in remembrance of their fallen leader.
 (1) *syn: somber; sober; staid*   *ant: jovial; frivolous*
 (2) *syn: ceremonious; reverential*

13. **tedious** (tē´ dē əs) *adj.* tiresome because of dullness or length
Making a thousand tissue-paper flowers for the parade float was a *tedious* process.
syn: monotonous; wearisome   *ant: fascinating; interesting; motivating*

14. **ungainly** (un gān´ lē) *adj.* lacking grace; clumsy
She is too *ungainly* to become a professional ice skater.
syn: awkward; lumbering   *ant: nimble; graceful*

15. **vilify** (vil´ ə fī) *v.* to make vicious statements about
Before the election, politicians on both sides *vilified* each other's presidential candidate.
syn: malign; denigrate; smear   *ant: praise; laud; compliment*

EXERCISE I – Words in Context

Using the vocabulary list for this lesson, supply the correct word to complete each sentence.

1. The spy threw the _____ onto the roof of the building, pulled the rope tight, and then scaled the wall.

2. No one said a word during the _____ memorial service.

3. Marcus _____ into his own memories while thinking of an idea for a story.

4. During the protest, activists held signs that _____ the officers of the corporation.

5. A signed permission slip is _____ for any student going on the field trip.

6. On the highway lay the _____ of an unlucky animal.

7. The _____ driver honked his horn and yelled rude comments when the funeral procession slowed him down.

8. The tiny village was a[n] _____ center of trade that eventually became the largest port city on the coast.

9. The child _____ the sand castle with one swipe of his hand.

10. The _____ child seems to trip over the lines on the floor tiles.

11. Making a New Year's resolution, Angela vowed total _____ from junk food.

12. Late for the show, Paige _____ through her dresser in search of the missing earring.

13. The blacksmith heated the metal to make it _____.

14. Her _____ job is to stuff thousands of envelopes with sales flyers.

15. The superhero prevented the _____ of Earth by redirecting the wayward comet toward the sun.

EXERCISE II – Sentence Completion

Complete the sentence in a way that shows you understand the meaning of the italicized vocabulary word.

1. At the library, Rachel *delved*…

2. Dominic had to *rummage* through the trash bin when…

3. During the *incipient* stages of the disease, symptoms are…

4. To prevent the *annihilation* of the planet, the hero must…

5. In many cultures, the *entrails* of livestock are…

6. Donald exercised a total *abstinence* for processed meat after he…

7. If the worker fails to follow the *mandatory* instructions, then he or she will…

8. Jade gave her *solemn* word that she would…

9. She *vilifies* anyone who…

10. Sergio *grappled* with his conscience while deciding…

11. It did not bother the *callous* man to see…

12. For being sarcastic with his mother, Brett was given the *tedious* chore of…

13. The hurricane *obliterated*…

14. He used a *pliable* sheet of plastic to…

15. Laughter broke out when the *ungainly* dancer…

EXERCISE III – Prefixes and Suffixes

Study the entries and use them to complete the questions that follow.

The suffix –*[c]ation* means "act of" or "result of."
The suffix –*er* means "one who does."
The suffix –*ity* means "state of" or "quality of."
The suffix –*ness* means "state," "quality," or "condition."

Use the provided prefixes and suffixes to change each root word so that it completes the sentence correctly. Then, keeping in mind that prefixes and suffixes sometimes change the part of speech, identify the part of speech of the new word by circling N for a noun, V for a verb, or ADJ for an adjective.

1. (pliable)   The _____ of the building's metal frame allows the structure to move slightly to absorb shock from earthquakes.
   N   V   ADJ

2. (vilify)   Politicians will endure some degree of _____ for any decision they make because there are two sides to everything.
   N   V   ADJ

3. (grapple)   The _____[s] stepped into the ring and glared at each other before the match began.
   N   V   ADJ

4. (callous)   His general _____ toward others seems to be a result of a difficult, abusive childhood.
   N   V   ADJ

EXERCISE IV – Critical Reading

The following reading passage contains vocabulary words from this lesson. Carefully read the passage and then choose the best answers for each of the questions that follow.

Of all the unsolved puzzles in the world, The Voynich Manuscript is among the most intriguing. The ancient book, written by an unknown author sometime between 1400 and 1600, is filled with mysterious symbols that resemble no alphabet on Earth and with strange illustrations of unknown people and plants. In five
5 hundred years, no one has been able to translate the obscure language or break the secret code. Drawings of unearthly plants, unknown celestial bodies, and people bathing among complex networks of pipes have generated many theories about the origin of the 260-page document, but no single theory seems to have any more weight than the others.

10 Since book dealer Wilfrid Voynich purchased the manuscript in 1912, many experts have **delved** into its strange content in search of some type of pattern. Even top military codebreakers have **grappled** with the indecipherable manuscript without result. Codebreaking computers have been assigned the **tedious** chore of analyzing the frequency of recurring symbols while scholars conducted more
15 thoughtful analyses of the text. The work produced a single, somewhat complicating, find: the patterns of the characters in the manuscript are unlike any in European languages. This find has prompted some cryptographers to suggest that the symbols are, in fact, Chinese code, because contact between European and Asian civilization before the fifteenth century has been recorded.

20 To scholars and experts, the illustrations are just as baffling as the cryptic language. Of the many plants depicted, many of which appear to be herbs having pharmaceutical value, only two have been identified as known plants. Some theories suggest the book is about *alchemy*, the medieval, quasi-scientific search for a way to turn lead into gold or the secret of physical immortality, but the illustrations
25 and layout of the manuscript are nothing like those of typical alchemy books of the time. The astrological diagrams further obscure the origin and purpose of the book; few of the drawings of stars, planets, and constellations seem to correspond with any known configurations.

Some codebreakers suggest that somewhere, perhaps buried in a vault or **oblit-**
30 **erated** by time, there exists—or once existed—a key to the Voynich Manuscript. The key might contain the algorithm the author used to encrypt the language of the book, much like the "rules" a modern computer programmer would use to encrypt, and later decrypt, an email message. While the impossible riddle of the manuscript shapes the willingly **pliable** imaginations of historians, language experts, and
35 ancient conspiracy theorists, some experts have a much simpler theory, though one **vilified** by those who dedicate considerable time to deciphering the book—that the Voynich Manuscript is nothing but an elaborate hoax.

1. As used in line 12, *grappled* most nearly means
   A. seized.
   B. encountered.
   C. hurdled.
   D. hoisted.
   E. struggled.

2. The pages of the Voynich Manuscript do not contain
   A. drawings of constellations.
   B. symbols thought to be Chinese in origin.
   C. depictions of people.
   D. pictures of herbs, some of which have been identified.
   E. music written for unknown instruments.

3. *Alchemy,* according to the passage, is
   A. the purpose of the Voynich Manuscript.
   B. not entirely scientific.
   C. a dangerous profession.
   D. a medieval style of writing.
   E. the search for herbs having pharmaceutical applications.

4. The best substitute for the word *pliable* in line 34 would be
   A. one-track.
   B. stubborn.
   C. impressionable.
   D. curious.
   E. overworked.

5. The author of the passage would most likely agree with which of the following statements?
   A. Further analysis might uncover the secret of the Voynich Manuscript.
   B. The Voynich Manuscript is undoubtedly a hoax.
   C. The Voynich Manuscript probably originated in Asia.
   D. Several theories offer the best explanations of the manuscript.
   E. The discoveries of the cryptographers are of primary importance.

Lesson Fifteen

1. **analogous** (ə nal′ ə gəs) *adj.* similar or parallel in certain ways
   Some people say that modern athletes are *analogous* to Roman gladiators.
   syn: comparable; related   *ant: dissimilar; unrelated*

2. **cleave** (klēv) *v.*   1. to split with a sharp instrument
                        2. to cling together
   (1) Using a butcher knife, he *cleaved* the steak and then wrapped the pieces in paper.
   (2) Survivors of the disaster *cleave* together for emotional support.
   (1) *syn: chop; slice*
   (2) *syn: adhere; unite*   *ant: repel; separate*

3. **derogatory** (di rog′ ə tôr ē) *adj.* belittling; disparaging
   Her *derogatory* remarks were not helpful to the student who lacked confidence.
   syn: critical; depreciatory   *ant: complimentary; flattering*

4. **distraught** (di strôt′) *adj.* extremely troubled or agitated; worried
   Many students were *distraught* when the pop quiz was announced.
   syn: distressed; upset   *ant: content; comfortable*

5. **exemplary** (ig zem′ plə rē) *adj.* worthy of imitation; setting a good example
   The organization awards scholarships to students who show *exemplary* citizenship.
   syn: commendable; admirable   *ant: inexcusable; reprehensible*

6. **homogeneous** (hō mə jē′ nē əs) *adj.* having or consisting of similar parts throughout
   My school instituted *homogeneous* class groupings arranged by ability.
   syn: uniform   *ant: heterogeneous; mixed*

7. **inadvertent** (in əd vûr′ tnt) *adj.* accidental; unintentional
   Numerous safety features prevent an *inadvertent* missile launch.
   syn: unintended; unplanned   *ant: intentional; deliberate*

8. **muddle** (mud′ l) *v.* to make confusing or unclear; to bungle
   Joe's inability to follow directions completely *muddled* the science experiment.
   syn: complicate; jumble; mess up   *ant: clear up; clarify*

9. **onomatopoeia** (on ə mat ə pē´ ə)   *n.*   the use of a word that sounds like the action or object it denotes
The words "bang" and "buzz" are examples of *onomatopoeia.*

10. **pompous** (pom´ pəs)   *adj.*   showing excessive self-esteem or vanity
The *pompous* celebrity felt that he should not have to make a reservation to eat at the upscale restaurant.
syn: portentous; conceited; overblown   *ant: modest; humble; shy*

11. **prowl** (proul)   *v.*   to move about stealthily, as though hunting or quietly searching
The lion *prowled* through the tall grass, quickly closing in on the zebra.
syn: lurk; stalk   *ant: march; parade; strut*

12. **raze** (rāz)   *v.*   to destroy so as to make level with the ground
The vengeful army *razed* the rebel hideout and took everyone prisoner.
syn: level; flatten

13. **stealthy** (stel´ thē)   *adj.*   acting with silence, caution, and secrecy
The *stealthy* invasion force overwhelmed the guards before they had a chance to sound the alarm.
syn: furtive; surreptitious; clandestine   *ant: obvious; unconcealed*

14. **throng** (throng)   *n.*   a crowded group of people or things
When Jason opened his store on the morning of the sale, he was pleased to see a *throng* of customers waiting outside.
syn: host; mass; multitude; horde

15. **vex** (veks)   *v.*   1. to annoy or disturb
                          2. to agitate mentally; to worry
(1) The squeaky wheels of her coworker's office chair *vexed* her.
(2) The lump on his neck *vexed* him until a doctor assured him that it was nothing.
(1) *syn: irk; irritate; aggravate*   *ant: please; delight; soothe*
(2) *syn: trouble; torment*   *ant: relieve; comfort*

EXERCISE I – Words in Context

Using the vocabulary list for this lesson, supply the correct word to complete each sentence.

1. Even while running, the _____ ninja created no more than a whisper of noise.

2. The angry fan shouted _____ comments when a player's error caused the home team to lose.

3. The _____ aviator acted and spoke as though he were the greatest pilot who had ever lived.

4. The trip would have gone quickly, but a detour due to road construction forced a[n] _____ tour of the scenic countryside.

5. To the advertising agency, getting people to purchase a product is _____ to fishing.

6. The tornado _____ several homes on the street, leaving only a few pieces of foundation standing above the ground.

7. The _____ child cried when she became lost in the shopping mall.

8. The guide used a machete to _____ through the thick vines blocking the trail.

9. The comic book relies heavily on instances of _____, especially during fight scenes in which punches are accompanied with the words "whap" or "thud."

10. The difficult riddle _____ her because she was certain that it had a very simple answer.

11. The company rewarded Mike's _____ performance by increasing his salary.

12. The thieves _____ throughout the upscale neighborhood in their old blue van, noting the presence of any security systems or watchdogs.

13. A[n] _____ of spectators stood and cheered whenever their team scored.

14. The speech would have been great if the speaker had not _____ the introduction.

15. Connor stirred the chocolate chips into the cookie batter until the dough became a[n] _____ mix.

EXERCISE II – Sentence Completion

Complete the sentence in a way that shows you understand the meaning of the italicized vocabulary word.

1. *Derogatory* remarks do not help...

2. Vicious guard dogs *prowled*...

3. Because of the company's *inadvertent* release of account numbers and personal information over the Internet, customers were advised to...

4. The child *cleaved* to her mother when...

5. If the boss *muddles* her instructions, the workers might...

6. The *pompous* man refused to...

7. The comment *vexed* everyone because it is unusual for Brandon to...

8. Critics claim that the new tax is *analogous* to...

9. The school chose an *exemplary* student to...

10. *Onomatopoeia* is often used when a writer wants to...

11. In order to be more *stealthy*, she wore...

12. A *throng* of angry villagers stormed the royal palace when...

13. Eric became *distraught* when...

14. After adding sugar and powdered drink mix to the water, she made the mixture *homogenous* by...

15. Using bulldozers, the workers *razed*...

EXERCISE III – Prefixes and Suffixes

Study the entries and use them to complete the questions that follow.

The suffix –*ive* means "tending to."
The suffix –*y* means "quality of" or "condition of."
The suffixes –*er* and –*or* mean "one who does."
The suffix –*ist* means "doer of" or "follower of."

Use the provided prefixes and suffixes to change each root word so that it completes the sentence correctly. Then, keeping in mind that prefixes and suffixes sometimes change the part of speech, identify the part of speech of the new word by circling N for a noun, V for a verb, or ADJ for an adjective.

1. (analogous) The depressing _____ likened human existence to life in a rat maze.

    N   V   ADJ

2. (prowl) Last night, a[n] _____ broke into our garden shed and stole some tools.

    N   V   ADJ

3. (derogatory) The congressman refused to answer what he believed was a[n] _____ question.

    N   V   ADJ

4. (cleave) The company claims that its new _____ cut through meat like no others.

    N   V   ADJ

EXERCISE IV – Improving Paragraphs

Read the following passage and then answer the multiple-choice questions that follow. The questions will require you to make decisions regarding the revision of the reading selection.

(1) The world's dependence on fossil fuels has many people **distraught**. (2) The era of gasoline-powered automobiles seems to be closing in a way that is **analogous** to the end of the whaling era, when the near extinction of whales forced people to find a substitute for the whale oil used in machinery. (3) Luckily, if new discoveries fail to ease the transition, and we are stuck without fuel to power our vehicles, we can always fall back on a previous form of transportation—and no, that does not mean a horse and buggy.

(4) If you purchased a Doble automobile during the 1920s, it's likely that some people would have described you as **pompous**, some Dobles sold for as much as $25,000 per car, which equates to nearly $300,000 today. (5) The cars were made to such tight tolerances that they contained no gaskets, and they were as beautiful in styling as any luxury car of the time; however, the Doble's greatest feature was its time-tested means of propulsion: steam power.

(6) Stanley Steamer already had produced thousands of reliable steam-powered cars, but to be driven, the Steamers required up to an hour to warm-up while their fifteen-gallon boilers produced enough steam to make power. (7) Development of the internal combustion engine, particularly the gasoline engine, caused **throngs** of drivers to reject Steamers for vehicles that could be started and driven immediately. (8) Steamers were out of the race, but Dobles still had a chance.

(9) The Doble was an attempt to bridge the widening gap between gasoline and steam automobiles. (10) Unlike the Stanley Steamer, the Doble was ready to drive only minutes after firing the generator, a tiny blast furnace that rapidly heated two quarts of water at a time. (11) It also featured **exemplary** performance; a Doble could leave many modern automobiles in the dust and cruise at speeds near 100 miles per hour.

(12) Both Dobles and Steamers were simple, durable cars, owing to the simplicity of steam power. (13) Most steam car engines attached directly to the car's drive axle. (14) This simple setup allowed for fewer complicated parts by eliminating the need for a clutch or transmission. (15) The Doble's advanced, four-cylinder engine design had twice the water efficiency of the Steamer's two-cylinder engine. (16) Both of the vehicles offered a **stealthy** ride, because steam pistons produce whispers compared to noisy gasoline engines.

(17) Had the makers of the Steamer and the Doble been better salesmen than designers, steam cars might have been motoring options today; however, whether they would have been any better than gasoline cars is debatable. (18) They had their benefits, but steam cars were far from perfect—or efficient. (19) Making steam requires fire, and fire requires plenty of fuel—as much as an internal combustion engine. (20) In addition, water evaporates; a boiler on a steam car must be refilled constantly.

(21) Steam cars might be gone, but steam power is not. (22) Today, steam

turbines convert steam power to electricity in nuclear power plants. (23) Satellites fitted with miniature reactors have had modest success in the past. (24) If these little reactors can ever be made safe enough to put into automobiles, expect a return of steam power; however, while we are waiting, steam might be a much more comfortable alternative than lurching along in a buggy.

1. Which choice best identifies the error in sentence 4?
   A. *it's* should be *its*
   B. comma splice
   C. incorrect use of a dollar sign
   D. *automobile* should be capitalized
   E. incorrect pronoun

2. Choose the most appropriate introductory sentence for paragraph 3.
   A. Steam power is still used today, at power-production facilities.
   B. Many trains used steam power, like these cars made by the Doble Detroit and Stanley Steamer companies.
   C. The last form of steam power did not appear on boats and ships, but cars, like the Stanley Steamer.
   D. Built by the Doble Detroit Company from 1914 to 1932, the Doble was the most advanced steam-powered automobile sold commercially.
   E. The Doble was better than the Stanley Steamer in many ways.

3. Which revision demonstrates the best way to combine sentences 13 and 14 (shown below)?

   > Most steam car engines attached directly to the car's drive
   > axle. This simple setup allowed for fewer complicated parts
   > by eliminating the need for a clutch or transmission.

   A. Most steam car engines attached directly to the car's drive axle and this simple setup allowed for fewer complicated parts by eliminating the need for a clutch or transmission.
   B. The need for a transmission and clutch was eliminated by the steam car engines' simple design, in which fewer parts were needed because the engine and axle were attached.
   C. Most steam car engines attached directly to the car's drive axle, which eliminated the need for a clutch or transmission.
   D. Most steam car engines attached directly to the car's drive axle, but this simple setup allowed for fewer complicated parts by eliminating the need for a clutch or transmission.
   E. The attachment of the axle to the simply designed steam car engine eliminated all the extra parts that would have been needed for a transmission or a clutch.

4. If inserted after sentence 23, which sentence best helps to clarify the prediction in the concluding paragraph?
   A. Two of the satellites actually caused a panic when they fell out of orbit, but steam power remains a viable form of locomotion.
   B. This is proof that steam-powered satellites are on the drawing board, but years and years away from being used.
   C. In these compact systems, the reactor is the steam generator, and the steam is used to generate electricity, which powers the satellite.
   D. These little reactors can go and go, allowing satellites to last for many years in orbit while producing a minimal amount of pollution, since they are above Earth's atmosphere.
   E. In such a system, the steam needed to produce electricity is generated by the reactor before the power of which is converted into electricity.

Review

Lessons 13 – 15

EXERCISE I – Inferences

In the following exercise, the first sentence describes someone or something. Infer information from the first sentence, and then choose the word from the Word Bank that best completes the second sentence.

Word Bank

stealthy	inadvertent	luscious	oppressive
mandatory	indignant	incipient	ungainly

1. The skilled hunter was able to get within thirty feet of the unsuspecting deer.
   From this sentence, we can infer that the hunter is _____.

2. In some states, drivers can be pulled over for not wearing seatbelts.
   From this sentence, we can infer that wearing a seatbelt is _____ in some states.

3. Dan's face turned red, and he breathed through clenched teeth when he saw that the neighbor's dog had strewn garbage across the front lawn.
   From this sentence, we can infer that Dan is _____.

4. While dancing, Ed constantly bumps into other people, sometimes knocking them down.
   From this sentence, we can infer that Ed is _____.

5. After completing a twelve-mile march, the recruits were ordered to clean the barracks, wash their laundry, and then prepare for another march the same evening.
   From this sentence, we can infer that the recruits have a[n] _____ training routine.

EXERCISE II – Related Words

Some of the vocabulary words from lessons 13–15 have related meanings. Complete the following sentences by choosing the word that best completes the specified relationship. Some word pairs will be antonyms, some will be synonyms, and some will be words often used in the same context.

1. *Raze* most nearly means
    A. cite.
    B. delve.
    C. obliterate.
    D. muddle.
    E. vex.

2. A *virtuoso* has _____ skills or talents.
    A. cynical
    B. pompous
    C. inadvertent
    D. ungainly
    E. exemplary

3. *Ponderous* is synonymous with
    A. luscious.
    B. tedious.
    C. solemn.
    D. derogatory.
    E. indignant.

4. *Vilify* contrasts most with
    A. cite.
    B. extortion.
    C. derogatory.
    D. muddle.
    E. vex.

5. *Rummage* is similar in meaning to
    A. abstinence.
    B. onomatopoeia.
    C. cynical.
    D. vilify.
    E. delve.

6. *Unbridled* means nearly the opposite of
   A. indignant.
   B. ungainly.
   C. distraught.
   D. stealthy.
   E. pompous.

7. A *callous* person might make _____ statements that offend others.
   A. mandatory
   B. pliable
   C. tedious
   D. derogatory
   E. homogeneous

8. *Acquiesce* contrasts most with
   A. grapple.
   B. exemplary.
   C. prowl.
   D. utopia.
   E. abstinence.

9. If something *vexes* a person long enough, then he or she might become
   A. virtuoso.
   B. distraught.
   C. inadvertent.
   D. analogous.
   E. suffrage.

10. Under the *oppressive* regime, it was _____ for all citizens to hang pictures of the ruler in their homes.
    A. analogous
    B. utopia
    C. ungainly
    D. mandatory
    E. inadvertent

EXERCISE III – Crossword Puzzle

Use the clues to complete the crossword puzzle. The answers consist of vocabulary words from lessons 13 through 15.

Across

1. All students must attend the _____ assembly in the auditorium.
3. The _____ man acted as though everyone were beneath him.
5. She was _____ during her first few hours on in-line skates.
7. On the map, a tiny picture of a picnic table _____[s] the location of a campground.
11. The beef processing plant keeps the good meat and ships the _____ to a pet-food factory.
12. The Earth Defense Force fired a missile to _____ the incoming asteroid.
13. Residents near the chemical factory were evacuated after the plant reported a[n] _____ release of toxic gas.

Down

2. Nancy _____[d] the patio furniture and then brought it inside for the winter.
3. Unable to walk, the injured hiker was a[n] _____ burden to the hikers carrying him on the trail.
4. Headquarters selected three _____ soldiers to complete the very demanding mission.
6. The _____ customers demanded to know why their expensive, high-speed Internet connections were not working properly.
8. The queen never promised a[n] _____ to her subjects, but she did promise to reduce poverty and crime.
9. Families sometimes grow closer when they _____ together during times of crisis.
10. The mournful sound of bagpipes accompanied the _____ funeral procession.
14. The evasive criminal _____[ed] the detective by leaving personal clues for her at crime scenes.

EXERCISE III – Crossword Puzzle

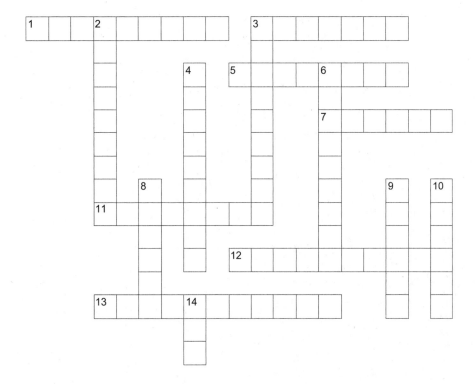

Lesson Sixteen

1. **anarchy** (an´ ər kē) *n.* lawlessness and disorder
   The small nation was a den of *anarchy* in the weeks following the revolution.
   syn: chaos   *ant: order*

2. **behoove** (bi hōōv´) *v.* to be necessary or proper for
   It is supposed to rain today, so it *behooves* you to carry an umbrella.
   syn: befit; suit

3. **contempt** (kən tempt´) *n.* 1. scorn and disrespect
                                        2. deliberate disobedience to a court of law
   (1) Some people on the team had feelings of *contempt* for the new player
       because he made the team without having to try out.
   (2) The defendant refused to stop shouting, so the judge charged him with
       contempt.
   (1) *syn: disdain; dislike*   *ant: admiration; esteem*

4. **diffusion** (di fyōō´ zhən) *n.* the process of scattering or dispersing
   To ensure a good *diffusion* of young fish, wildlife officials added them to
   several different parts of the lake.
   syn: dispersal; distribution   *ant: concentration*

5. **elusive** (i lōō´ siv) *adj.* difficult to capture, understand, or see
   The *elusive* animal has never been photographed in nature.
   syn: evasive; equivocal; unclear   *ant: direct; accessible; tangible*

6. **fanfare** (fan´ fâr) *n.* 1. a short, loud tune played on brass instruments
                                  2. a showy, public display
   (1) A *fanfare* of trumpets sounded as the royal family entered the ballroom.
   (2) After returning from the important mission, the astronauts were
       greeted with great *fanfare.*

7. **gullible** (gul´ ə bəl) *adj.* easily deceived or tricked
   The *gullible* boy truly believed that he had just purchased a designer watch
   for only twenty dollars.
   syn: naive; credulous   *ant: cynical; worldly*

8. **icon** (ī′ kon) *n.* 1. a visual representation, often a small picture
                   2. a person who receives great attention and devotion
                   3. an important, enduring symbol
   (1) A small *icon* depicting one of her heroes reminds her that she should always strive to be a better person.
   (2) The blockbuster movie turned the formerly unknown actor into a cultural *icon*.
   (3) The eagle is a major *icon* of the United States.
   (1) *syn: symbol*
   (2) *syn: idol; superstar*
   (3) *syn: hallmark; trademark*

9. **mangle** (mang′ gəl) *v.* to mutilate severely; to disfigure beyond recognition
Brianna had to pay for her textbook because her dog *mangled* it.
syn: deface; destroy   *ant: repair; mend*

10. **oblique** (ō blēk′) *adj.* 1. angled; slanting 2. indirect or misleading
   (1) The *oblique* roof allows rain and snow to fall off the building.
   (2) He attempted to change the subject by giving an *oblique* answer to our question.
   (1) *syn: slanted; sloping; tilted*
   (2) *syn: circuitous; twisting*   *ant: direct; straightforward*

11. **patriarchal** (pā trē är′ kəl) *adj.* pertaining to rule or leadership by men or fathers
In the *patriarchal* tradition, the eldest son inherited the farm.

12. **recourse** (rē′ kôrs **or** rē kôrs′) *n.* someone or something turned to for assistance
After losing the trial, his only *recourse* was to file an appeal with a higher court.
syn: resort; refuge

13. **sabotage** (sab′ ə täzh) *v.* to hinder normal operations by intentionally destroying something or tampering with the processes
The spy *sabotaged* the enemy's torpedo factory by removing parts from the machinery.
syn: disrupt; impair   *ant: assist; support*

14. **susceptible** (sə sep′ tə bəl) *adj.* easily influenced; likely to be affected
You are *susceptible* to chicken pox if you have never had it before.
syn: prone; liable; subject   *ant: impervious; resistant*

15. **usurer** (ū´ zhər ər) *n.* a person who loans money at excessive interest rates

No bank would give him a loan, so he turned to a *usurer*.

syn: loan shark; moneylender

EXERCISE I – Words in Context

Using the vocabulary list for this lesson, supply the correct word to complete each sentence.

1. The _____ gladly loans money, but borrowers pay back nearly twice the amount of the loan.

2. Her _____ response successfully changed the subject, but failed to answer the original question.

3. Moviegoers stared in _____ at the couple who refused to stop whispering throughout the entire film.

4. The Olympic runner received impressive _____ whenever she returned to her small hometown.

5. People who are _____ to motion sickness might have difficulty riding a roller coaster.

6. The con artist preys on _____ people who are willing to trust strangers.

7. If you want to pass the class, then it _____ you to take notes.

8. The dishonest mechanic _____ automobiles and then charged customers for the repairs.

9. The elephant and the donkey are major _____ of American politics.

10. The chemistry teacher explained the importance of proper _____ of the chemicals in the solution.

11. Separated from her family and friends, Gabrielle had no _____ during the difficult time.

12. Though famous, the _____ tycoon always seemed to be one step ahead of the reporters and photographers.

13. The first-grade teacher worried that the order in the classroom would deteriorate into _____ if she left the children alone for a few minutes.

14. The women's rights movement had made great changes to the formerly _____ society.

15. Charles accidentally _____ the rose bush with the lawnmower.

EXERCISE II – Sentence Completion

Complete the sentence in a way that shows you understand the meaning of the italicized vocabulary word.

1. The *oblique* question was meant to…

2. She has felt great *contempt* for him ever since…

3. The *gullible* man paid…

4. Bart *sabotaged* what would have been a pleasant family dinner when he…

5. The prime minister feared that *anarchy* and violence would consume the nation if…

6. To get out of debt, their only *recourse* was…

7. If the powdered mix does not achieve proper *diffusion*, the lemonade will…

8. The people portrayed on U.S. paper currency are *icons* of…

9. The *usurer* demanded…

10. If a lightning storm is approaching, it *behooves* you to…

11. The *elusive* man is nearly impossible to…

12. The old, dry barn is very *susceptible* to…

13. The spinning fan blades *mangled*…

14. The *fanfare* of approval prompted the gladiator to…

15. Irene challenged the *patriarchal* structure of the corporation by…

EXERCISE III – Prefixes and Suffixes

Study the entries and use them to complete the questions that follow.

The suffix –*ible* means "able to be."
The suffix –*ic* means "characteristic of" or "pertaining to."
The suffix –*ist* means "one who does" or "follower of."
The suffix –*ity* means "state of" or "quality of."

Use the provided prefixes and suffixes to change each root word so that it completes the sentence correctly. Then, keeping in mind that prefixes and suffixes sometimes change the part of speech, identify the part of speech of the new word by circling N for a noun, V for a verb, or ADJ for an adjective.

1. (anarchy)   The _____ believed that no forms of government
    should exist.

    N   V   ADJ

2. (gullible)   Nathan took advantage of the child's _____ by telling
    him that a nickel is worth more than a dime because it is larger in size.

    N   V   ADJ

3. (contempt) She was suspended for her _____ behavior in school.

    N   V   ADJ

4. (icon) Albert Einstein's wild hair and humble demeanor contributed to •
    his _____ recognition in both the scientific and popular media.

    N   V   ADJ

EXERCISE IV – Critical Reading

The following reading passage contains vocabulary words from this lesson. Carefully read the passage and then choose the best answers for each of the questions that follow.

Industry was booming at the start of the twentieth century; the American Industrial Revolution neared its peak, and factories churned around the clock to meet the demands of a growing pool of consumers. Though wages were minuscule and shifts were unbearably long, factory workers were simply happy to have jobs;
5 many of them were immigrants who came from places devoid of any opportunity whatsoever. Some families could not earn enough to sustain themselves, and other **gullible** people were cheated by employers who were actually **usurers**. These landlords or factory owners provided homes or loans and then demanded repayment in the form of many years of cheap labor, making the American dream **elusive** to the
10 workers. For people in these situations, the only **recourse** was to send children to work.

As labor unions had not yet formed, and the people who exploited unbridled capitalism had not yet been restrained, the government disregarded certain aspects of industry that today would be described as barbaric, especially child labor.
15 Child labor at the turn of the century bore no resemblance to a modern teenager's part-time job at a restaurant or shopping mall for some extra spending money. In 1900, nearly two million American children participated in full-time, backbreaking drudgery, and most of the children worked not for the newest MP3 player, but for money to help feed their parents and siblings.

20 To some barons of industry, children were naturally suited for certain jobs in factories. Children were small, so they were perfect for climbing into or working in confined spaces where adults could not go. Children also worked for low wages, so they were ideal for unskilled jobs that wasted the greater work capacity of adults; these jobs, however, were not easy.

25 Breathing air full of coal dust and rarely seeing the sun, children in coal mines worked from dawn until dusk opening and closing ventilation doors to keep air circulating beneath the ground. Some children maintained equipment, and by the end of the day, the young "greasers" were covered with soot and grease. Others emerged from the pits bleeding from the fingers and hunched permanently from
30 picking unburnable rocks out of coal piles. Some children avoided black-lung and rheumatism only to be **mangled** by heavy machinery.

The textile industry employed many young girls. Day after day, they worked for hours, breathing air laden with wool particles and standing so long that their feet became deformed. In mills, the air was dampened intentionally to prevent
35 breaks in the thread; the warm, damp air made the children **susceptible** to an assortment of lung diseases, the most rampant of which was tuberculosis. As materials reached various stages of completion, they were sent to tenement homes, where girls sewed all day with their mothers or siblings.

Glass factories were especially cruel for children; hot furnaces and tanks of
40 molten glass made temperatures unbearable for adults, let alone ten-year-olds. During twelve-hour shifts in temperatures exceeding 100 degrees, the children

reached into furnaces to extract red-hot trays of glass products. Flames and sparks scorched skin and blinded eyes. Missing eyebrows, dried faces, and singed hair were common features of the children and teenagers making bottles. Few working
45 children had time to go to school; they remained illiterate, unskilled, and locked into a particular job until they were injured, crippled, or killed.

Slowly but definitively, the American public acknowledged the dreadfulness of child labor. Committees formed across the nation, among them the National Child Labor Committee in 1904, and convinced states to restrict the worst forms of child
50 labor. Owing to worries that labor regulation would, unconstitutionally, give the government too much authority over private industry, proposals for Federal restrictions were rejected three times in 1916, 1918, and 1924. Finally, in 1938, the Fair Labor Standard Act limited child labor in mining and manufacturing.

1. As used in line 10, *recourse* most nearly means
   A. resort.
   B. surrender.
   C. idea.
   D. schedule.
   E. conclusion.

2. Which choice best identifies the purpose of paragraph 2?
   A. to describe the conditions in which child laborers worked
   B. to persuade readers that more action should be taken to eliminate child labor
   C. to show that previous generations were harder workers than present generations
   D. to inform audiences that child labor still exists
   E. to define *child labor* as it is used in the passage

3. The best substitute for the word *susceptible* as it is used in line 35 is
   A. invulnerable.
   B. prone.
   C. cater.
   D. carry.
   E. safe.

4. According to the passage, the federal government was hesitant to pass child labor restrictions because
    A. barons of industry bribed the judges on the Supreme Court.
    B. officials were too busy with the Spanish-American War and World War I.
    C. the plight of child labor affected only non-citizens.
    D. too much government regulation of private industry is unconstitutional.
    E. the state had already restricted the most severe forms of child labor.

5. The most appropriate title for this passage would be:
    A. The Complete History of American Child Labor.
    B. Minors and Miners: Child Labor in the Coal Industry.
    C. Child Labor in American Industry.
    D. Government Regulation of Child Labor.
    E. The Accomplishments of Children in America.

Lesson Seventeen

1. **amiable** (ā´ mē ə bəl) *adj.* friendly and likable
   The *amiable* student made friends easily.
   syn: affable; good-natured   *ant: offensive; unpleasant*

2. **baleful** (bāl´ fəl) *adj.* sinister; threatening
   The *baleful* tone of the villain's voice caused everyone to worry about what
   he had planned.
   syn: menacing; malevolent   *ant: comforting; encouraging*

3. **criterion** (krī tîr´ ē ən) *n.* a standard on which decisions can be based;
       a basis for comparison
   If he does not satisfy the *criterion* set forth by the teacher, he must repeat
   the class.
   syn: measure; touchstone

4. **devoid** (di void´) *adj.* completely lacking; empty
   His angry comment was *devoid* of logic but filled with passion.
   syn: bereft; without; deficient   *ant: filled; replete*

5. **dormant** (dôr´ mənt) *adj.* inactive as though asleep
   The volcano is *dormant,* but it could still erupt someday.
   syn: latent; resting   *ant: active; functional*

6. **eulogy** (yōō´ lə jē) *n.* an admiring speech or written tribute, usually
       for someone who has died
   Martin wrote a moving *eulogy* for his deceased uncle and read it during
   the funeral.
   syn: panegyric; encomium

7. **iconoclast** (ī kon´ ə klast) *n.* a person who attacks and seeks to destroy
       popular ideas or traditions
   Many critics consider Picasso an *iconoclast* because his painting style
   broke all the traditional rules.
   syn: agitator; revolutionary   *ant: conformist*

8. **instigate** (in´ sti gāt) *v.* to provoke
   The rebels *instigated* the coup by convincing citizens to join the fight.
   syn: initiate; set off   *ant: quell; suppress; allay*

9. **marginal** (mär´ jə nəl) *adj.* barely meeting the lowest standard; of
    minimal quality
    She passed the class, but with *marginal* grades.
    syn: borderline; negligible   *ant: superior; excelling*

10. **peerless** (pîr´ lis) *adj.* without equal; matchless
    Her *peerless* performance during the audition won her the lead in the play.
    syn: incomparable; unrivaled   *ant: average; common*

11. **prone** (prōn) *adj.* 1. lying face down
                             2. having a tendency
    (1) Hidden behind the bunker, the *prone* soldier radioed for air support.
    (2) She is *prone* to overspending, so her parents no longer allow her to use
    the credit card.
    (1) *syn: prostrate*   *ant: supine*
    (2) *syn: inclined; subject*   *ant: unlikely; inapt*

12. **repel** (ri pel´) *v.* to drive away; to ward off
    The spray *repels* mosquitoes and other biting insects.
    syn: repulse; fend off   *ant: attract; draw*

13. **serene** (sə rēn´) *adj.* very calm; untroubled
    The hypnotist's *serene* voice helped the patient to relax.
    syn: tranquil; peaceful   *ant: frantic; restless; distraught*

14. **tactless** (takt´ lis) *adj.* careless about the feelings of others; rude
    The *tactless* man freely announces people's flaws, often causing them mild
    embarrassment.
    syn: indiscreet; inconsiderate; gauche   *ant: tactful; polite; considerate*

15. **unfathomable** (un fath´ ə mə bəl) *n.* difficult or impossible to
    understand
    No one has been able to explain the *unfathomable* message in the ancient
    scrolls.
    syn: incomprehensible; indecipherable   *ant: straightforward; simple; basic*

EXERCISE I – Words in Context

Using the vocabulary list for this lesson, supply the correct word to complete each sentence.

1. The committee gathered to determine a single _____ for the winning essay.

2. Bobby lay _____ beneath the hedges as he waited to ambush his sister with a snowball.

3. My uncle sometimes seems like a[n] _____ because he purposely breaks norms and conventions whenever he possibly can.

4. Jared seems quiet and reserved, but he is a[n] _____ person once you get to know him.

5. Dan's _____ afternoon at home was rudely interrupted by the thundering sound of the neighbor's motorcycle.

6. The contractor warned the homeowners that he could do only a[n] _____ repair job on the roof for such a low fee.

7. Kelly's desire to go skydiving is _____ because she is afraid of heights.

8. Though World War II ended more than sixty years ago, the Nazi flag is still a[n] _____ symbol of evil.

9. She burst into tears while reading the _____ during the funeral service.

10. The castle guards _____ the invaders by pouring hot oil on their heads from high above.

11. The barren Martian landscape is completely _____ of life.

12. Pam _____ a confrontation by spreading gossip about both of the two rivals.

13. The manufacturer has a reputation for making products of _____ quality—hence, the exorbitant price tags.

14. Pointing out the flaw in her painting in front of everyone was a[n] _____ thing to do.

15. If the disease remains _____, then the carrier will not show any symptoms.

EXERCISE II – Sentence Completion

Complete the sentence in a way that shows you understand the meaning of the italicized vocabulary word.

1. Their home was *devoid* of laughter after…

2. Matt's *tactless* friends embarrassed him when…

3. If someone is *prone* to motion sickness, then he or she should…

4. By mentioning the controversial subject, he accidentally *instigated*…

5. The previous winning essay is the *criterion* for…

6. The *unfathomable* crime prompted elected representatives to…

7. Rosa is an *amiable* person who enjoys…

8. The *peerless* chess master challenged…

9. In her latest book, the *iconoclast* criticizes…

10. Using the garden hose, Lesley *repelled*…

11. The lightweight jacket offered only *marginal* protection from…

12. The acorn lay *dormant* until…

13. During the *eulogy*, the reader described…

14. When the captain saw the *baleful* storm clouds over the horizon, he ordered…

15. He struggled to remain *serene* when…

EXERCISE III – Prefixes and Suffixes

Study the entries and use them to complete the questions that follow.

The prefix *un–* means "not" or "opposite of."
The suffix *–ancy* means "condition of" or "quality of."
The suffix *–ant* means "performer of."
The suffix *–ize* means "to become" or "to cause to become."

Use the provided prefixes and suffixes to change each root word so that it completes the sentence correctly. Then, keeping in mind that prefixes and suffixes sometimes change the part of speech, identify the part of speech of the new word by circling N for a noun, V for a verb, or ADJ for an adjective.

1. (eulogy)   She _____ her deceased brother with a heartrending poem.

    N V ADJ

2. (dormant)   Bears spend the winter months in a state of _____ known as hibernation.

    N V ADJ

3. (amiable)   The _____ waiter seemed to be quite annoyed when we made a simple request for water.

    N V ADJ

4. (repel) The dog's flea collar is _____ to biting insects.

    N V ADJ

EXERCISE IV – Critical Reading

The following reading passage contains vocabulary words from this lesson. Carefully read the passage and then choose the best answers for each of the questions that follow.

One of the greatest proofs that anyone can make it big is the one-hit wonder—
an artist or group whose single work, usually a song, becomes widely known and
catapults the artist to temporary fame. After its brief burst of life, the song typically
remains in the collective consciousness of the public, but the artists seem to fade
5 into oblivion except for the tiny reference beneath the feature songs flowing down
the TV screen during late-night infomercials selling "Best of…" music compilations
for, if you call now, only $19.95! If you need examples, ponder *Macarena* by Los
Del Rio, or *Who Let the Dogs Out?* by Baha Men.

The one-hit wonder is nothing new; the first, perhaps oldest, one-hit wonder
10 to hit the music scene made his debut way back in the 80s—the *1680s*! Even if
you do not realize it, you probably, at least once, have heard *Canon in D* by Johann
Pachelbel, a German composer born in 1653. Pachelbel's *Canon* is a simple, **serene**
tune that features a repetitive sequence of eight notes, usually played by a low-
sounding cello or tuba. Violins or similar-sounding instruments accompany the
15 continuo with a flowing melody, fairly lively but very mellow. The piece lay **dormant** for nearly three centuries before a 1970 recording by the Paillard Chamber
Orchestra of Paris turned it into one of the most well-known songs of the baroque
musical era. *Canon* can now be heard in numerous pop songs, commercial advertisements, movies, and television shows.

20 Another one-hit wonder, the French composer Paul Dukas, created a hit that
might be more familiar to younger generations. *The Sorcerer's Apprentice*, written in
1897, became legendary when brooms came to life and marched around with water
buckets as a consequence of Mickey Mouse's magic spell-gone-wrong in the Disney
classic, *Fantasia.*

25 Not all one-hit-wonder compositions have **amiable** themes. In 1937, *Carmina
Burana*, the famous cantata (work of both voice and orchestra) by German composer Carl Orff, shocked audiences with its driven, **baleful** chorales thematic of
the fickleness of fortune, vice, and the fleeting nature of life. Though dismissed
by some critics as musically **marginal**, the stirring music **repelled** obscurity to
30 live on through the popular culture of the present, though most often in films and
television.

No one said that an artist must be a musical **iconoclast** as a **criterion** for
becoming a one-hit-wonder; arguably, some of the most popular songs to date have
been **devoid** of any real musical value or special uniqueness. What seems to mat-
35 ter is whether a tune can **instigate** its own repetition in your head for hours—or
days—on end. Perhaps that is what truly explains where one-hit wonders go when
they fade away—they go into hiding!

1. According to the passage, Pachelbel's *Canon in D* is not
   A. the work of possibly the earliest one-hit wonder.
   B. more than 200 years older than *Carmina Burana*.
   C. the most popular song by Johann Pachelbel.
   D. remade using damaged documents showing the original score.
   E. written for more than one voice (musical instrument).

2. In paragraph 2, *continuo* refers to
   A. the translation for *Canon*.
   B. the conductor.
   C. the last portion of the song.
   D. the tuba.
   E. the repetitive sequence.

3. The first sentence in the concluding paragraph suggests that a musical *iconoclast* would be likely to
   A. turn down status as a one-hit wonder.
   B. produce a distinctive musical composition.
   C. copy past compositions and sell them as his or her own.
   D. be a one-hit wonder.
   E. ignore new trends in music and remain within traditional guidelines.

4. As used in line 16, *dormant* most nearly means
   A. peaceful.
   B. asleep.
   C. unused.
   D. boisterous.
   E. popular.

5. The tone of the passage is best described as
   A. thoughtfully guarded.
   B. accepting and understanding.
   C. informal and witty.
   D. admiring and respectful.
   E. derisive and critical.

Lesson Eighteen

1. **assimilate**   (ə sim´ ə lāt)   *v.*   1. to absorb mentally
    2. to be absorbed into a larger group
    (1) He *assimilated* the customs of the natives after living with them for several years.
    (2) During the early nineteenth century, European immigrants *assimilated* more easily than Asian immigrants.
    (1) *syn: learn; incorporate*   *ant: deny; reject*
    (2) *syn: conform; integrate*   *ant: rebel; resist*

2. **colloquial**   (ke lō´ kwē əl)   *adj.*   characteristic of informal speech
    Many people use the *colloquial* word "fridge" instead of "refrigerator."
    syn: conversational   *ant: formal; proper; stilted*

3. **dirge**   (dûrj)   *n.*   a mournful hymn or poem
    She wrote a *dirge* in honor of the fallen hero and read it at the funeral service.
    syn: elegy; requiem

4. **epithet**   (ep´ ə thet)   *n.*   a word or phrase used to describe a person or thing, sometimes abusively
    Alexander earned his *epithet*, "the Great," by conquering much of the ancient world.
    syn: nickname

5. **festoon**   (fe stōōn´)   *v.*   to decorate with a garland; to decorate as one would with a garland
    To decorate for the homecoming dance, students *festooned* the gymnasium with streamers.
    syn: drape; swathe

6. **hamper**   (ham´ pər)   *v.*   to prevent progress or movement
    The heavy ball and chain *hampered* the fleeing prisoner.
    syn: hinder; impede   *ant: assist; facilitate*

7. **induce**   (in dōōs´)   *v.*   to bring about; to cause
    The label on the poisonous chemical instructs people to *induce* vomiting if the substance is accidentally swallowed.
    syn: stimulate; provoke   *ant: prevent; thwart*

8. **matriarchal** (mā´ trē ar kəl) *adj.* pertaining to rule or leadership by
     women or mothers
   A council of female elders governs the *matriarchal* tribe.

9. **niche** (nich) *n.* 1. a recess in the wall 2. an activity or a position well
     suited to a person's interests or abilities
     (1) A modern art statue stands in a *niche* across from the couch.
     (2) After years of job-hopping, Meg finally found her *niche* as a private
         investigator.
     (1) *syn: alcove; nook; cubbyhole*
     (2) *syn: forte; metier; strong point*

10. **perfidy** (pûr´ fi dē) *n.* deliberate betrayal of trust or faith
    The dishonest cashier had been stealing money from the register for
    weeks until a surveillance camera reorded her *perfidy*.
    syn: treachery; duplicity; treason   *ant: loyalty; faithfulness*

11. **prophetic** (prof et´ ik) *adj.* foretelling events as though supernaturally
    He made a *prophetic* statement about the upcoming election.
    syn: telling; predictive; foreshadowing

12. **rehabilitate** (rē hə bil´ i tāt) *v.* to restore or be restored to good health
      or productive life
    After the accident, she *rehabilitated* herself by exercising every day.
    syn: recuperate; mend   *ant: degenerate; weaken*

13. **simultaneous** (sī məl tā´ nē əs) *adj.* occurring or existing at the same
      time
    An argument occurred when two shoppers made a *simultaneous* grab for
    the last item on the shelf.
    syn: concurrent; coincident   *ant: successive; progressing*

14. **surmise** (sər mīz´) *v.* to conclude from little evidence; guess
    From a distance, she *surmised* that the person lying on the beach was
    simply sleeping.
    syn: conjecture; speculate; presume

15. **vigilante** (vij ə lan´ tē) *n.* one who enforces the law or punishes
      criminals without having authority to do so
    The police gave up their search, but the *vigilante* eventually tracked down
    the killer.

EXERCISE I – Words in Context

Using the vocabulary list for this lesson, supply the correct word to complete each sentence.

1. Tim felt _____ pain and embarrassment when he accidentally walked into a glass door.

2. The mother makes most of the major decisions in the _____ household.

3. She was inspired to write a mournful _____ when she heard the news of her grandfather's death.

4. The woman had not yet given birth two weeks past her due date, so the doctor _____ labor and delivered the baby.

5. The foreign family _____ into the new society by learning the language and becoming citizens.

6. They realized how _____ his statement had been when it came true hours later.

7. The bounty hunter examined the tracks on the trail and _____ that the criminal had passed through only hours before.

8. Jeremy _____ his bedroom walls with posters of the cars he dreamed of having someday.

9. The teacher asked that students refrain from using _____ language in their research papers.

10. Exhausted after two years of working without a day off, Miranda _____ herself during a two-week vacation to the Caribbean.

11. The _____ in the wall contains a phone booth and a vending machine.

12. The _____ captured a drug dealer and forced him to provide the name of his boss.

13. There was little guessing as to the meaning of the mobster's _____, "Scarface."

14. In one of the greatest _____ to befall the nation, a scientist sold weapons technology to the enemy.

15. The naval blockade _____ the transfer of supplies to the enemy.

EXERCISE II – Sentence Completion

Complete the sentence in a way that shows you understand the meaning of the italicized vocabulary word.

1. To help new students *assimilate*, the teacher asks...

2. His *perfidy* made him rich, but he could never...

3. After being injured, Dustin *rehabilitated* his shoulder by...

4. The church bells played a *dirge* when...

5. The swift current of the river *hampered*...

6. In the *matriarchal* organization, men are...

7. A political *epithet* on the bumper sticker was an insult to anyone who...

8. The oracle warned the king about a *prophetic* vision in which...

9. The *vigilante* promised to...

10. Before Jack found his *niche* in art, he did not think...

11. To *induce* thought in the students, the teacher asked...

12. The English professor's use of *colloquial* language surprised the students because...

13. From the animal's poor health, Molly *surmised*...

14. The theater avoids scheduling *simultaneous* show times to prevent...

15. Before the festival, townspeople *festooned*...

EXERCISE III – Prefixes and Suffixes

Study the entries and use them to complete the questions that follow.

The suffix *–al* means "pertaining to" or "characteristic of."
The suffix *–ic* means "characteristic of" or "pertaining to."
The suffix *–ion* means "act of," "state of," or "result of."
The suffix *–ism* means "system" or "system of."

Use the provided prefixes and suffixes to change each root word so that it completes the sentence correctly. Then, keeping in mind that prefixes and suffixes sometimes change the part of speech, identify the part of speech of the new word by circling N for a noun, V for a verb, or ADJ for an adjective.

1. (colloquial) "Cool" is an overused _____ that can be avoided by simply choosing a better adjective.

    N   V   ADJ

2. (epithet)   The _____ circus poster listed such performers as "The Flying Mondello" and "Lisa of the Lions."

    N   V   ADJ

3. (surmise)   He retracted his first _____ that the movie sequel would be terrible when he saw that it featured one of his favorite actors.

    N   V   ADJ

4. (assimilate) After the purchase and the subsequent _____ of several smaller companies, the corporation became the largest of its type.

    N   V   ADJ

EXERCISE IV – Improving Paragraphs

Read the following passage and then answer the multiple-choice questions that follow. The questions will require you to make decisions regarding the revision of the reading selection.

(1) If you see a beetle crawling across your floor, think twice about squashing it: it might just explode.

(2) The bombardier beetle inhabits a special **niche** in the animal kingdom. (3) It is the only bug that is a chemical weapons expert. (4) Its specialty is binary agents, or pairs of chemicals that remain harmless until combined.

(5) Flat and round, the bombardier beetle looks like the average beetle, with a heavy shell protecting its wings and body. (6) It, in fact, refers not to a single species of beetle, but any beetles who can expel an unpleasant, volatile chemical from its abdomen. (7) To aim the shot, the beetle can swivel the turret up to 270 degrees—and the bug is a proven sharpshooter. (8) The beetles use this chemical cannon as a defensive weapon, usually against its mortal enemy and fellow ground-dweller, the ant.

(9) But a simple chemical spray is much simpler than what a bombardier beetle really does inside. (10) If the discharge is watched in slow motion, an observer would notice that the chemical is mist and vapor, and that it is in the process of exploding; the detonation, in fact, makes an audible popping sound. (11) At 212 degrees Fahrenheit, the temperature at which water boils, the blast is fatally hot to many insects.

(12) How does this happen in a bug that does not even use its wings very often? (13) The amazing process begins with specialized glands in the beetle's body that produce two separate chemicals, *hydroquinones* and *hydrogen peroxide* (as you would use to clean a cut on your skin). (14) Combined in the beetle, these chemicals would react if the beetle did not also produce a chemical that **hampers** the reaction. (15) Once "loaded," the beetle stores the stable mixture in an internal reservoir until it **surmises** that something is a threat.

(16) To fire its weapons, the beetle forces the stable mixture into a "blast chamber" near the tip of its abdomen. (17) In the chamber, the stable chemicals mix with a *catalyst*, a chemical that speeds up reactions. (18) The catalyst **induces** a rapid reaction between the hydroquinones and peroxide; so rapid, in fact, that part of the mixture explodes during its **simultaneous** discharge from the specialized "turret" on the tip of the beetle's abdomen.

(19) What could be the next discovery of insect warfare? (20) Moth missiles? (21) Grasshopper grenades? (22) If more bugs like the bombardier beetle are discovered, we might need to consider a peace treaty between the bomber bugs and the army ants.

1. Which revision best clarifies the underlined portion of sentence 6 (shown below)?

   It, in fact, refers not to a single species of beetle, but any beetles who can expel an unpleasant, volatile chemical from its abdomen.

   A. The name "bombardier beetle," in fact, refers not to a single beetle which
   B. "Bombardier beetle," in fact, refers to all bugs that
   C. "Bombardier beetle," in fact, refers not to a single species of beetle, but any beetle that
   D. The behavior, in fact, refers not to a single species of beetle, but any beetles who
   E. It in fact refers not to one beetle, but all beetles who

2. Sentence 7 is best written to follow
   A. sentence 4.
   B. sentence 10.
   C. sentence 13.
   D. sentence 18.
   E. sentence 22.

3. Which choice best revises sentence 9 while fulfilling the intent of the original sentence?
   A. The beetle's defense mechanism is more complicated than the beetle itself.
   B. There's more than meets the eye regarding the beetle's combination of chemicals.
   C. Few beetles can boast of a complex, binary chemical weapons system.
   D. The interior of the bombardier beetle is extremely complicated.
   E. The beetle's complex defense involves much more than simply spraying a chemical.

4. Sentence 12 should be revised or deleted because
   A. it contains information irrelevant to the subtopic.
   B. its formal style contrasts with the rest of the paragraph.
   C. paragraphs cannot begin with questions.
   D. beetles use their wings every day, according to the passage.
   E. as it is, the sentence belongs in the introductory paragraph.

Review

Lessons 16 – 18

EXERCISE I – Inferences

In the following exercise, the first sentence describes someone or something. Infer information from the first sentence, and then choose the word from the Word Bank that best completes the second sentence.

Word Bank

matriarchal	gullible	marginal	baleful
tactless	oblique	prophetic	elusive

1. Had he scored one point lower on the test, Mike would have failed for the year.
   From this sentence, we can infer that Mike received a[n] _____ grade on the test.

2. Though the car had high mileage, Chris bought it because the dealer said the car runs better as it gets older.
   From this sentence, we can infer that Chris is _____.

3. Greta was elated to have won the art contest until Allison told her that she had won only because the judges felt sorry for her..
   From this sentence, we can infer that Allison is _____.

4. Years later, Susan would see the scene from her dream take place in reality.
   From this sentence, we can infer that Susan's dream was _____.

5. The fish is believed to exist in great numbers, but one is rarely sighted.
   From this sentence, we can infer that the fish is _____.

EXERCISE II – Related Words

Some of the vocabulary words from lessons 16–18 have related meanings. Complete the following sentences by choosing the word that best completes the specified relationship. Some word pairs will be antonyms, some will be synonyms, and some will be words often used in the same context.

1. *Induce* is synonymous with
    A. diffusion.
    B. dormant.
    C. repel.
    D. hamper.
    E. instigate.

2. *Rehabilitate* contrasts most with
    A. behoove.
    B. mangle.
    C. festoon.
    D. surmise.
    E. serene.

3. *Eulogy* is most similar in meaning to
    A. anarchy.
    B. vigilante.
    C. niche.
    D. dirge.
    E. usurer.

4. *Marginal* work is not likely to be described as
    A. peerless.
    B. elusive.
    C. tactless.
    D. prophetic.
    E. devoid.

5. *Sabotage* carried out by a friend is
    A. amiable.
    B. peerless.
    C. perfidy.
    D. simultaneous.
    E. anarchy.

6. *Baleful* contrasts most with
   A. susceptible.
   B. tactless.
   C. unfathomable.
   D. amiable.
   E. perfidy.

7. A *gullible* person is _____ to the ill intentions of others.
   A. patriarchal
   B. susceptible
   C. marginal
   D. unfathomable
   E. matriarchal

8. *Matriarchal* is the opposite of
   A. diffusion.
   B. colloquial.
   C. prophetic.
   D. patriarchal.
   E. susceptible.

9 The nation *assimilated* other cultures, but _____ those who sought to destroy it.
   A. instigated
   B. festooned
   C. repelled
   D. surmised
   E. behooved

10. The closest antonym for *hamper* is
   A. mangle.
   B. behoove.
   C. instigate.
   D. festoon.
   E. oblique.

EXERCISE III – Crossword Puzzle

Use the clues to complete the crossword puzzle. The answers consist of vocabulary words from lessons 16 through 18.

Across

1. The author of the _____ novel suffered a fate very similar to that of the story's hero.
5. The alien spacecraft used an advanced technology that was _____ to the greatest scientists on Earth.
8. When the explorers ran out of fuel many light years from the nearest outpost, their only _____ was to land on an uncharted planet and wait for help.
9. Jeremy _____[d] his mountain bike when he crashed into a tree.
10. The _____ warned his clients about the consequences of not repaying the loan on time.
13. Simply mentioning the hated name in public nearly _____[d] a riot.
14. An incorrect engine adjustment _____[ed] the performance of the team's race car.
15. Students thought the teacher was _____ of mercy when he assigned a lengthy reading assignment over the holiday weekend.

Down

2. People who are especially _____ to sunburn should wear good sunscreen and limit their exposure to the sun.
3. To _____ economic growth in the area, the city decreased taxes for small businesses.
4. After the road rage incident, Howard had to take anger management classes to learn how to remain _____ while driving.
6. The tiny nation turned the president's visit into an event of great _____.
7. The _____ caught the cat burglar, tied him up, and deposited him on the steps of the police station.
11. The act of _____ was an attempt to shut down the enemy's shipbuilding factory.
12. The living room wall has a[n] _____ in which to put the television and stereo.

EXERCISE III – Crossword Puzzle

Lesson Nineteen

1. **antagonism** (an tag´ ə niz əm) *n.* a state of hostility
   Antagonism among club members prevents any progress during the monthly meetings.
   syn: opposition; enmity; rivalry   *ant: amity; friendliness*

2. **aversion** (ə vûr´ zhən) *n.* a strong dislike
   A single bout of food poisoning gave her an *aversion* to seafood for the rest of her life.
   syn: distaste; hatred   *ant: fondness; liking*

3. **cavalier** (kav ə lîr´) *adj.* showing arrogant disregard or indifference
   n. a gallant gentleman or knight, especially one serving royalty
   (1) She made the *cavalier* assertion that the hurricane victims were at fault for building homes near the coast.
   (2) The *cavalier* escorted the princess when she traveled throughout the kingdom.
   (1) *syn: offhand; inconsiderate; lofty*   *ant: understanding; considerate*
   (2) *syn: chevalier*

4. **diatribe** (dī´ ə trīb) *n.* bitter and abusive criticism
   Dad launched into a *diatribe* about shoddy work when the roof started to leak.
   syn: denunciation; tirade   *ant: praise*

5. **disencumber** (dis en kum´ bər) *v.* to free from burden or difficulty
   The new, automatic dishwasher *disencumbered* the kitchen staff and allowed them to focus on food preparation.
   syn: relieve; unburden   *ant: burden; encumber*

6. **evanescent** (ev ə nes´ ənt) *adj.* lasting only a short time; vanishing
   She allowed herself only an *evanescent* moment of anger before she diverted her energies to solving the new problem.
   syn: transient; ephemeral; fleeting   *ant: permanent; persistent*

7. **gala** (gā´ lə **or** ga´ lə) *n.* a festive event
   adj. festive and celebratory
   (n) The successful manufacturer hosted a *gala* to celebrate a record-breaking year.
   (a) The charitable organization held a *gala* ball to raise money for its cause.
   (n) *syn: festival; celebration*

8. **insignia** (in sig´ nē ə) *n.* a badge indicating rank or membership
The private saluted the officer wearing a general's *insignia*.
syn: emblem

9. **morbid** (môr´ bid) *adj.* gruesome; grotesque
Certain writings of Edgar Allan Poe contain *morbid* images of suffering and death.
syn: perverse; macabre; grisly   *ant: charming; delightful*

10. **perturb** (pər tûrb´) *v.* to disturb
Bobby's insistence on sliding backwards down the stair rail *perturbed* his mother.
syn: agitate; upset   *ant: calm; soothe*

11. **prosecute** (pros´ i kūt) *v.* to bring criminal action against; to put on trial
The state *prosecuted* the man who caused a fatal automobile accident.
syn: indict; arraign   *ant: pardon; exonerate; absolve*

12. **spelunker** (spē lung´ kər) *n.* a person who explores caves
The *spelunker* always brings food and extra batteries when he explores new caves.

13. **surreal** (sə rēl´) *adj.* 1. marked by strange images and combinations
                                    2. having dreamlike qualities
(1) The lounge is painted with *surreal* patterns that make people dizzy if they stare too long at them.
(2) The low, rolling fog beneath the full moon made the sky look *surreal*.
(1) *syn: fantastic; bizarre; weird*   *ant: mundane; common*

14. **tyrannical** (ti ran´ i kəl) *adj.* unreasonably severe and oppressive
The *tyrannical* king had most of his critics imprisoned or executed.
syn: totalitarian; despotic; domineering   *ant: permissive; tolerant*

15. **unassailable** (un ə sāl´ ə bəl) *adj.* 1. impossible to disprove or question
                                                  2. impossible to attack or conquer
(1) The tabloid reporters struggled to find anything controversial in the politician's *unassailable* record.
(2) The *unassailable* castle wall protected the village for three centuries.
(1) *syn: incontrovertible; indisputable; sound*   *ant: tenuous; questionable*
(2) *syn: invincible; invulnerable; impregnable*   *ant: defenseless; weak; susceptible*

EXERCISE I – Words in Context

Using the vocabulary list for this lesson, supply the correct word to complete each sentence.

1. Her _____ comment offended many of the people in the room.

2. No one could break her _____ devotion to the cause.

3. Pleas for mercy had no effect on the _____ dictator.

4. Randy's pencil tapping _____ everyone in the room.

5. Joel has exhibited a[n] _____ to dogs ever since one bit him.

6. The _____ on her uniform indicated that she was a pilot.

7. They had been enemies for years, but they eventually decided to end their _____ and became friends.

8. The airplane ride was a[n] _____ experience for the child who had never even been in an automobile.

9. The kind stranger _____ the elderly woman by carrying her heavy grocery bag.

10. After making a costly mistake, the employee had to endure a[n] _____ from his boss.

11. Deep within the cavern, the _____ discovered an underground river.

12. The city marked its three-hundredth year with an anniversary _____.

13. For hours, she struggled to remember the _____ idea that had passed through her mind earlier.

14. The district attorney decided not to _____ the thief who spent three days stuck in someone's chimney.

15. The _____ Halloween costume was so disturbing that Steve was not sure he should wear it around children.

EXERCISE II – Sentence Completion

Complete the sentence in a way that shows you understand the meaning of the italicized vocabulary word.

1. Heather scolded Tim for his *morbid* sense of humor after…

2. *Antagonism* has existed between the two neighbors ever since…

3. The *surreal* painting reminded…

4. When the child saw the man wearing the *insignia*, she assumed…

5. After the election, a *gala* was held to…

6. Autumn accused her parents of being *tyrannical* when…

7. If the scuffmark on the floor truly *perturbs* you, then you should…

8. She abandoned her *cavalier* attitude about charity when…

9. The theory will be *unassailable* until new technology allows scientists to…

10. The court might *prosecute* a minor as an adult if…

11. When Mark heard the *diatribe* left on his answering machine, he realized…

12. Because he wanted to *disencumber* his team for the championship game, the injured player told…

13. Dwayne developed an *aversion* to camping when…

14. The *spelunker* began to worry when…

15. Devon's *evanescent* term of office ended abruptly when…

EXERCISE III – Prefixes and Suffixes

Study the entries and use them to complete the questions that follow.

The suffix –*ist* means "one who does" or "follower of."
The suffix –*ity* means "state of" or "quality of."
The suffix –*ize* means "to become" or "to cause to become."
The suffix –*or* means "one who does."

Use the provided prefixes and suffixes to change each root word so that it completes the sentence correctly. Then, keeping in mind that prefixes and suffixes sometimes change the part of speech, identify the part of speech of the new word by circling N for a noun, V for a verb, or ADJ for an adjective.

1. (prosecute)   The _____ told the judge that the defendant was a threat to everyone.

    N   V   ADJ

2. (antagonism) Pat _____[ed] his brother one time too many and found himself punished with double his usual chores.

    N   V   ADJ

3. (morbid)   The _____ of the scenes in the horror film is not appropriate for children.

    N   V   ADJ

4. (surreal)   One of the most famous paintings by the _____ Salvador Dali depicts melting watches, one of which hangs on the limb of a tree.

    N   V   ADJ

EXERCISE IV – Critical Reading

The following reading passage contains vocabulary words from this lesson. Carefully read the passage and then choose the best answers for each of the questions that follow.

Antagonism between relatives is nothing new. As long as humans have been around, they have been battling their families for everything, from food, to money, to love. When King Harold of England fought with his brother Tostig, the prize was power.

5   Harold and Tostig did not begin as royalty; they were simply members of the powerful Godwin family. Allegedly, in 1017, King Canute, who favored the Godwins, had seized the throne and immediately killed most of the men who had helped him. He replaced the murdered staff members with trusted friends, who included members of the Godwin family.

10   The Godwins, especially Harold, toiled over the next few years to increase their political influence. When the earl of Northumbria died in 1055, and left the northern region of England leaderless, Harold pushed his brother Tostig into the position.

    Tostig, unfortunately, was not cut out for the job. His **tyrannical** reign, dur-
15 ing which he imposed martial law and inflicted severe punishments, **perturbed** the other powerful families in the area, and they conspired against him. Harold realized that the angry families could serve his own interests better than his brother could, so he sided with them. Tostig fled during a revolt in 1065, but he would return in 1066, with Harold's throne as his target.

20   Tostig did not return alone. He brought Norwegian King Harald Hardraade ("Harald the Ruthless") and a large group of Viking warriors with him. Harald claimed that he had the right to the English throne since one of his relatives had been king.

    By the time Tostig returned, Harold Godwin had become the king of England.
25 Accompanied by an army made up mostly of peasant farmers, Harold met Tostig and Hardraade at Stamford Bridge, northeast of the city of York. In the weeks before, Tostig and the Norwegians had stormed through Northumbria, defeating the forces of the very families with whom Harold had sided against Tostig. The triumphs made the invaders overly optimistic. Believing that they were meeting at
30 the bridge to receive one hundred English hostages, Hardraade and Tostig left most of the soldiers at their ships. When Tostig and Hardraade arrived at the bridge, they were surprised to find Harold—and a sizable force of armed soldiers.

    A battle ensued between Harold's army and the few unprepared, unarmored Vikings. According to legend, a lone Norwegian soldier held Harold's forces off on
35 the bridge until one of Harold's **cavaliers** sailed beneath it and stabbed the defiant warrior with a spear. The single-handed holdout is probably an embellishment, but it is true that the Vikings, with their raven **insignia** raised high, hung on as long as they could before Harold's army overwhelmed them. No longer **unassailable**,
40 Tostig and Hardraade were both cut down in battle. Leaderless, the remaining sol-
diers agreed to cease attacks on England and were allowed to depart. King Harold's decision to pursue power instead of loyalty seemed to have paid off.

1. Which factor contributed most to Harold and Tostig's affiliation with royalty?
    A. Harold and Tostig were the sons of King Canute.
    B. King Canute was a cousin to the Godwins.
    C. Tostig's father was Harald Hardraade's brother-in-law.
    D. The Godwin family enjoyed King Canute's favor.
    E. Harold's father purchased the family's nobility.

2. Tostig's governing style was *tyrannical*, which means that Tostig was
    A. supportive of art and technology.
    B. unreasonably oppressive.
    C. confusing to foreign visitors.
    D. carefully attentive to law.
    E. overly concerned with religion.

3. Before the battle of Stamford Bridge, Tostig and Harald Hardraade thought they were *unassailable* because
    A. they wore magic armor forged in the ovens of Woden.
    B. the Viking army did not typically require any armor.
    C. King Harold's army consisted of peasants.
    D. they had already beaten everyone who had sided against Tostig.
    E. they had won several victories during their invasion of England.

4. From the final sentence, a reader can infer that
    A. Tostig had believed all along that Harold should be king.
    B. Harold would probably make the same choice again.
    C. Harold defended the throne, but he was a bad king.
    D. Harald Hardraade had never wished to invade England.
    E. Harold regretted his decision and wished Tostig would forgive him.

5. Which choice best identifies the main idea of the passage?
    A. Harold should have been loyal to his brother Tostig.
    B. The Norwegians had the most valid claim to the English throne.
    C. Even brothers turn against each other in their pursuit of power.
    D. Stamford Bridge was an unassailable battle site.
    E. Tostig was forced to be Earl of Northumbria.

Lesson Twenty

1. **ardent** (är´ dnt) *adj.* emotionally intense; passionate
   She had such an *ardent* desire to help the sick that she became a doctor.
   syn: fervent; devoted   *ant: indifferent; unenthusiastic*

2. **cower** (kou´ ər) *v.* to curl up in fear
   The dog *cowered* at the sound of its owner's commanding voice.
   syn: cringe; recoil   *ant: swagger*

3. **devious** (dē´ vē əs) *adj.* evasive and deceitful
   The *devious* thief posed as a cable repairman to sneak into the mansion.
   syn: sneaky; crafty; underhanded   *ant: forthright; straightforward*

4. **doggerel** (dog´ ər əl) *n.* crude, comical, or inferior verse
   She likes to send birthday cards that contain some type of silly *doggerel*.

5. **imp** (imp) *n.* a mischievous person or creature
   Susan is certain that her younger brother is an irksome *imp* whose daily goal is to make her angry.
   syn: prankster; rascal

6. **invalid** (in´ və lid) *n.* someone who is incapacitated due to injury or illness   1. incapacitated due to illness or injury
   (in val´ id) *adj.*   2. not officially valid

   (n) Refusing to allow his injuries to turn him into an *invalid*, Troy continued with the painful therapy.

   (a.1) Soldiers with minor wounds were treated, and *invalid* soldiers were sent to a hospital away from the front lines.

   (a.2) Tom has an *invalid* driver's license because he forgot to renew it last month.

   (n) *syn: convalescent; paralytic*
   (a.1) *syn: bedridden; disabled; infirm*   *ant: healthy; well*
   (a.2) *syn: null; void*   *ant: legitimate; legal*

7. **multifarious** (mul tə fâr´ ē əs) *adj.* having great variety
   Her *multifarious* interests led her to join nearly every club the school offered.
   syn: diverse; varied   *ant: uniform; homogenous*

8.   **munificent**   (mū nif´ i sənt)   *adj.*   very generous in giving
Upon his death the *munificent* entrepreneur left his entire fortune to charity.
syn: lavish; unsparing; liberal   *ant: miserly; stingy*

9.   **oracle**   (ôr´ ə kəl)   *n.*   a wise person thought to be able to predict the future
The king sent the warrior to consult with the *oracle* before undertaking the dangerous quest.
syn: auger; seer; prophet

10.   **posterity**   (po ster´ i tē)   *n.*   all future generations or descendants
The wealthy industrialist built the library for *posterity*.

11.   **pretentious**   (prē ten´ shəs)   *adj.*   showing excessive or unjustified self-importance or merit
The *pretentious* student acted as though winning a single essay contest made her a famous scholar.
syn: ostentatious; pompous   *ant: modest; unassuming*

12.   **procure**   (prō cūr´)   *v.*   to acquire through special effort
The supply clerk *procures* equipment for the soldiers in the battalion.
syn: obtain

13.   **resilient**   (ri zil´ yənt)   *adj.*   able to recover quickly
The *resilient* plant can survive floods, drought, and insect damage.
syn: durable; hardy   *ant: fragile; weak*

14.   **rivulet**   (riv´ yə lit)   *n.*   a small stream or brook
The children fish for trout in the *rivulet* that flows through the forest.
syn: run; creek

15.   **thwart**   (thwôrt)   *v.*   to prevent something from happening
The hero *thwarted* the villain's evil plan.
syn: foil; frustrate; impede   *ant: assist; support*

EXERCISE I – Words in Context

Using the vocabulary list for this lesson, supply the correct word to complete each sentence.

1. Friends tease Wyatt for his _____ attachment to sports because his happiness seems to depend on athletes he has never met.

2. Young Hanna slept with a[n] _____ array of stuffed animals.

3. The _____ man believed his painting was a masterpiece.

4. A sudden rainstorm _____ Jasmine's plans for a walk.

5. Isabel _____ beneath the sheets when the shadows frightened her at night.

6. After a spinal cord injury turned her into a[n] _____, Katherine decided to make the most of her remaining abilities.

7. After being struck by the car, the _____ dog healed completely within weeks.

8. Her _____ scam cheated hundreds of people out of their hard-earned money.

9. The _____ warned everyone that something terrible was about to happen.

10. Andre knew that a pipe must have burst when he saw the _____ flowing across the lawn.

11. Book reviewers criticized the pop star's book, saying that it was nothing more than a collection of _____ that is neither moving nor entertaining.

12. The parents took hundreds of photographs of the children to save for _____.

13. Mike thanked his _____ grandmother for assisting him financially during the difficult time.

14. No one claimed responsibility for the broken window, so Marco blamed it on an imaginary _____.

15. Before she could open the ice cream shop, Audrey _____ a business license.

EXERCISE II – Sentence Completion

Complete the sentence in a way that shows you understand the meaning of the italicized vocabulary word.

1. The *multifarious* collection in her living room contains…

2. The magazine editor discards most of the *doggerel* e-mailed from readers because…

3. The unnecessary use of *pretentious* words might cause…

4. Three days of steady rainfall turned the *rivulet* into…

5. The general inspired *ardent* loyalty among the troops because…

6. If your library card is *invalid*, you will…

7. To feed the refugees, the relief workers *procured*…

8. The child *cowered* when…

9. The *devious* illusion caused unsuspecting victims to…

10. Mikey was called an *imp* because…

11. Investors called the stockbroker an *oracle* because…

12. The *resilient* virus is especially dangerous because…

13. When travelers ask for shelter, the *munificent* king provides…

14. To *thwart* future burglaries, the bank manager hired…

15. For *posterity*, grandmother…

EXERCISE III – Prefixes and Suffixes

Study the entries and use them to complete the questions that follow.

The suffix –*ence* means "state of" or "quality of."
The suffix –*ate* means "to become" or "to cause to become."
The suffix –*ment* means "result of."
The suffix –*ness* means "state," "quality," or "condition."

Use the provided prefixes and suffixes to change each root word so that it completes the sentence correctly. Then, keeping in mind that prefixes and suffixes sometimes change the part of speech, identify the part of speech of the new word by circling N for a noun, V for a verb, or ADJ for an adjective.

1. (procure)   After the _____ of some dry wood, the campers can build a fire.

    N   V   ADJ

2. (invalid)   The Supreme Court voted to _____ the unconstitutional law.

    N   V   ADJ

3. (pretentious) Her intentional use of complicated words gave her an air of _____.

    N   V   ADJ

4. (resilient)   Pat's _____ shocked everyone when he stood up, unharmed, after falling from the ladder.

    N   V   ADJ

EXERCISE IV – Critical Reading

The following reading passage contains vocabulary words from this lesson. Carefully read the passage and then choose the best answers for each of the questions that follow.

Never fear—Gilgamesh is here!

Gilgamesh?

That's right, Gilgamesh—the **munificent** superhero who felled the powerful Humbaba in the cedar forest!

5   Maybe you have never heard of Gilgamesh; after all, he did go out of style about five thousand years before Batman or Wonder Woman.

Shortly before the American Civil War, twelve clay tablets were discovered among other ancient texts in the region now known as Iraq. On the tablets is inscribed the first known epic poem in the history of the world, though a revised
10   version. The author, whose name is also carved into the clay, is thought to have recorded the poem around the year 1000 BC, though fragments of the legend on which the poem is based appear on relics as old as 2000 BC.

The poem tells the tale of Gilgamesh, the namesake of a Sumerian king thought to have reigned over the city of Uruk several centuries before the epic
15   was written. Though his **pretentious** ego and overconfidence are similar to those of other ancient heroes, such as Achilles and Beowulf, Gilgamesh's superpowers, notably his strength and endurance, are more similar to those of modern comic book heroes.

Using his great powers, Gilgamesh embarks on several missions, the first, and
20   seemingly most unnecessary, being to destroy Humbaba, the protector of the forest. Next, as a punishment for rejecting the advances of a goddess, Gilgamesh and his sidekick, Enkidu, must battle and slay the Bull of Heaven. Angered over their dead bull, the gods curse Enkidu with sickness. To Gilgamesh's great woe, the **invalid** Enkid perishes.

25   The death of Enkidu prompts Gilgamesh to embark on a long journey in search of the secret to immortality, driven by both grief over his friend and an **ardent** desire to be remembered forever.

Some of the epic's **multifarious** themes emerge during the journey. At one point, an innkeeper attempts to dissuade Gilgamesh from his quest, explaining that
30   people should simply learn to enjoy and appreciate the simpler things in life, like food and family. The logic fails to **thwart** the headstrong hero. Gilgamesh eventually finds Utnapishtim, an immortal, and asks him for the secret of eternal life. He first orders Gilgamesh to stay awake for an entire week. The hero fails. Utnapishtim offers Gilgamesh a second chance, this time to retrieve a plant that grants immor-
35   tality. Gilgamesh **procures** the plant only to leave it unattended and lose it to a snake.

Had the author of Gilgamesh known that the hero was going to gain five thousand years of **posterity**, perhaps he or she would have dressed the hero up a little, maybe with a mask or a cape, or added some of the action common to mod-
40   ern comic **doggerel**, like an oxcart crashing through the window—make that stone wall—of a an ancient Babylonian coffeehouse. It really does not matter, though; the real lesson of the *Epic of Gilgamesh* is quite clear: If you want immortality, carve your message into clay tablets.

1. According to the passage, the hero Gilgamesh is named after
    A. the innkeeper.
    B. a hero related to Achilles.
    C. a city in ancient Sumeria.
    D. an ancient king.
    E. the archaeologist who discovered the clay tablets.

2. As used in line 15, *pretentious* means the opposite of
    A. eccentric.
    B. intolerable.
    C. humble.
    D. frightened.
    E. quiet.

3. According to the author of the passage, the *Epic of Gilgamesh*
    A. contains age-old themes.
    B. is based on a materialistic hero.
    C. lacks literary value.
    D. is largely unknown because pieces of the clay tablets are missing.
    E. is more exciting than modern comic books.

4. As used in line 35, *procures* most nearly means
    A. dismisses.
    B. obtains.
    C. steals.
    D. forfeits.
    E. finds.

5. The primary intent of the passage is to
    A. prove the advanced language of ancient Sumeria.
    B. inform about two obscure civilizations.
    C. explain connections between Gilgamesh and modern superheroes.
    D. dispute theories over the origins of Gilgamesh and Uruk.
    E. suggest the longevity of superheroes as fictional characters.

Lesson Twenty-One

1. **atrophy** (at´ rə fē) *v.* to waste away or deteriorate due to disease or disuse
   After the accident, his muscles *atrophied* during his four months of bed rest.
   syn: wither; degenerate   *ant: thrive*

2. **capsize** (kap´ sīz) *v.* to overturn or cause to overturn
   Eddie *capsized* the canoe when he stood up to get a better look at the shore.
   syn: roll; upset

3. **dearth** (dûrth) *n.* a lack or scarcity
   The prolonged drought caused a *dearth* of food during the winter.
   syn: deficiency; shortage; paucity   *ant: glut; surplus; plethora*

4. **disdain** (dis dān´) *n.* a feeling of strong disrespect and dislike
                        v. to regard with arrogant contempt
   (n) He has great *disdain* for people who complain about things but fail to take any action.
   (v) She *disdains* anyone who did not experience the same harsh childhood that she did.
   (n) *syn: contempt; scorn*   *ant: admiration; esteem*
   (v) *syn: despise; spurn*   *ant: admire; respect*

5. **embezzle** (em bez´ əl) *v.* to steal property one has been entrusted to protect
   The bank manager secretly *embezzled* tens of thousands of dollars over the course of several years.
   syn: misappropriate

6. **inept** (in ept´) *adj.* lacking grace, skill, or judgment; incompetent
   The *inept* security guard allowed thieves to steal five cars off the dealer's lot during his first night on the job.
   syn: bungling; clumsy   *ant: adept; skilled*

7. **iota** (ī ō´ tə) *n.* a tiny amount
   She was so tired of arguing that she refused to give the subject an *iota* of thought.
   syn: bit; trace; scintilla   *ant: abundance*

8. **omnipotent** (om nip´ ə tənt) *adj.* having unlimited power
The dictator strived to maintain an *omnipotent* image among his oppressed citizens.
syn: supreme; all-powerful   *ant: powerless; weak*

9. **piecemeal** (pēs´ mēl) *adj.* built in small stages; made one piece at a time
                              adv. in stages; one piece at a time
(adj) Budget cuts caused a *piecemeal* construction of the new wing of the school.
(adv) Over a period of two decades, Johnny built the car *piecemeal* from parts he found in the scrap pile behind the automobile factory.
(adv) *syn: gradually*   *ant: suddenly*

10. **precipice** (pres´ ə pis) *n.* a very steep cliff
The climber stopped to rest about halfway up the *precipice*.

11. **prostrate** (pros´ trāt) *adj.* lying face down
                            v. to lie or cause to lie face down
(a) She knew something was wrong at the bank when she looked through the window and saw that the tellers and customers were *prostrate*.
(v) The suspect *prostrated* himself and put his hands behind his head when the police threatened to release their dog.
(a) *syn: prone*   *ant: supine*

12. **relic** (rel´ ik) *n.* an old object of historic or religious significance
The fire at the museum destroyed several priceless *relics*.
syn: artifact; remnant

13. **staunch** (stänch) *adj.* dedicated; steadfast; loyal
She is a *staunch* believer that success is simply a measure of determination.
syn: faithful; committed; unwavering   *ant: fickle; undetermined*

14. **sumptuous** (sump´ chōō əs) *adj.* of great luxury, expense, and quantity; luxurious
The king's coronation ball began with a *sumptuous* feast.
syn: lavish; opulent; extravagant   *ant: meager; paltry; inadequate*

15. **unscathed** (un skāthd´) *adj.* not harmed or injured
Miraculously, he walked away from the terrible accident *unscathed*.
syn: unhurt; unharmed   *ant: wounded; hurt*

EXERCISE I – Words in Context

Using the vocabulary list for this lesson, supply the correct word to complete each sentence.

1. The action hero jumped off the speeding truck just before it sailed over the edge of the _____ and exploded on the rocks far below.

2. The warehouse manager _____ company funds by selling products falsely listed as damaged and then pocketing the cash.

3. The gardener's back yard features a[n] _____ collection of the world's most beautiful exotic flowers.

4. The spy remained _____ in the tall grass to evade detection.

5. A massive wave _____ the fishing boat.

6. The alien invaders were thought to be _____ until a simple human disease—the common cold—wiped them out.

7. Luckily, everyone escaped from the burning house _____.

8. When she awoke from a three-year coma, she could barely walk because her muscles had _____.

9. The machine was so large that it had to be transported _____ and reassembled at the new location.

10. Craig treated the younger employee with _____ because he felt that she was a threat to his job.

11. Her _____ opinion is not likely to change soon.

12. The dank basement apartment had a _____ of sunlight because it had no windows.

13. She did not experience a[n] _____ of guilt because she felt her actions were completely appropriate.

14. The ancient tomb contained many _____ of a long extinct civilization.

15. They fired the _____ worker for making a mistake that nearly put the company out of business.

EXERCISE II – Sentence Completion

Complete the sentence in a way that shows you understand the meaning of the italicized vocabulary word.

1. After his raft *capsized*, the castaway was forced to...

2. Loretta's parents felt *disdain* for their daughter's decision to...

3. When Ben saw the *relic* from his childhood, it reminded...

4. The *omnipotent* queen aroused fear among her subjects because...

5. He was *prostrated* by...

6. The *staunch* supporters of the cause refused...

7. Experiencing a *dearth* of creativity, the novelist could not...

8. An *iota* of concern for your health now can prevent...

9. The space station must be assembled *piecemeal* because...

10. After his arrest, the employee claimed that he *embezzled* money because...

11. Guests complimented the host's *sumptuous* taste when...

12. To prevent cars from falling over the *precipice*, the highway department installed...

13. The sculptures survived the flood *unscathed*, but...

14. His legs *atrophied* during...

15. The *inept* babysitter allowed...

EXERCISE III – Prefixes and Suffixes

Study the entries and use them to complete the questions that follow.

The suffix –*[i]tude* means "condition of" or "state of."
The suffix –*ence* means "state of" or "quality of."
The suffix –*ful* means "full of" or "having."
The suffix –*ment* means "result of."

Use the provided prefixes and suffixes to change each root word so that it completes the sentence correctly. Then, keeping in mind that prefixes and suffixes sometimes change the part of speech, identify the part of speech of the new word by circling N for a noun, V for a verb, or ADJ for an adjective.

1. (disdain)   The students stopped chatting during the lesson when they saw the teacher's _____ stare.
   N   V   ADJ

2. (omnipotent) The super-villain thought he could achieve _____ if he perfected the indestructible bionic suit.
   N   V   ADJ

3. (inept) Even a small amount of _____ can be fatal for people working at the refinery.
   N   V   ADJ

4. (embezzle) The company estimates a loss of $2 million last year as a result of _____.
   N   V   ADJ

EXERCISE IV – Improving Paragraphs

Read the following passage and then answer the multiple-choice questions that follow. The questions will require you to make decisions regarding the revision of the reading selection.

(1) If you ever find yourself stranded in the wilderness, you might need to build a fire to keep warm, purify water, cook food, or signal for help. (2) With a little knowledge, and a match or a lighter, someone who is **inept** at lighting even a barbeque grill should be able to build a roaring fire. (3) Consequently, you should always have one or the other while camping, hiking, or traveling through the woods. (4) A pocketknife and some rope can also be useful if you have them when you need them. (5) An **iota** of thought now might save your life later.

(6) Before you begin, make certain that you actually need a fire. (7) If you can keep warm with a blanket, or you have food that requires no cooking, then the energy you expend building a campfire might be better used elsewhere.

(8) Using your foot or hand, clear the sticks and leaves from an area on the ground several feet in diameter. You want a campfire—not a forest fire.

(9) Your fire is going to start small and grow in stages. (10) First, gather small, dry twigs, leaves, and any other material that will readily burn. (11) The dead branches jutting from the bottom of an evergreen tree are excellent tinder, especially during rainy weather. (12) Snap off a few handfuls of these, and gather up any dried-out needles as well. (13) Do not overlook bird's nests and wasp's nests (preferably abandoned).

(14) Business cards and coupons will work very well, and even cash can be burned in a crisis. (15) If you have a knife, you can make tinder by shaving strips from larger pieces of wood. (16) Remember to select dead, dry wood instead of green, moist wood.

(17) Keep your tinder dry while you gather larger pieces of kindling. (18) Once the fire is burning, it is risky to build it **piecemeal** because it might burn out while you search for the next stage of fuel.

(19) The kindling should be slightly larger than the tinder, but smaller than fuel wood. (20) Look for dry sticks up to one inch in diameter. (21) Find slightly larger ones for stage three, and keep an eye out for fuel wood, which will be the largest pieces. (22) You do not want your fire to burn out while you are looking for wood.

(23) Carry your fuel and kindling back to your fire pit and make a little bed with the fine tinder. (24) Place a small, fluffy pile in the center, and ensure the remainder is ready to add when the pile ignites. (25) Over the tinder pile, construct a small tepee of kindling, but leave an opening through which to put the lighter or matches. (26) Ensure that the tepee is stable enough to stand on its own.

(27) Light the tinder. (28) If you run out of matches and the flame dies, **prostrate** yourself and gently blow on the smoldering tinder while you add more to the pile. (29) If you can make it hot enough, the tinder will ignite.

(30) When you see a flame, simply add increasingly larger pieces of tinder and kindling as it grows. (31) However the tepee structure should allow the fire to continue on its own. (32) When the fire looks stable, go and gather larger pieces of fuel wood. (33) Look for fallen trees that are dry, not rotten. (34) When the fire becomes an adequate size, simply add wood as necessary to maintain it.

1. Choose the best revision for the underlined portion of sentence 3 (shown below).

> <u>Consequently, you should always have one or the other</u> while camping, hiking, or traveling through the woods.

    A. For this reason, it is wise to carry matches or a lighter...
    B. Due to the risk, it is recommended that you always have a lighter...
    C. Because of this knowledge, you should always carry matches or a lighter...
    D. However, it is wise to carry matches or lighter...
    E. One or the other should always be with you...

2. Which would be the most appropriate introductory sentence for paragraph 5?
    A. A **staunch** believer in his or her own abilities can find tinder.
    B. If your locale has a **dearth** of tinder, check your wallet or purse for things that will burn.
    C. **Relics** that have been kept dry will also make great tinder.
    D. Motivate yourself with thoughts of the **sumptuous** feast you can cook over your fire.
    E. If you are in the rain, and your wallet is **unscathed**, you can use it for tinder.

3. Of the following choices, which shows the best way to combine sentences 30 and 31?
    A. When you see a flame, simply add increasingly larger pieces of tinder and kindling as it grows on its own due to the fact that the tepee structure...
    B. When you see a flame, simply add increasingly larger pieces of tinder and kindling as it grows throughout the tepee structure...
    C. When you see a flame, simply add increasingly larger pieces of tinder and kindling as it grows with the tepee structure...
    D. When you see a flame, simply add increasingly larger pieces of tinder and kindling as it (the flame) grows, although the tepee, structure...
    E. When you see a flame, simply add increasingly larger pieces of tinder and kindling as it grows, though the tepee structure...

4. If the passage were to be expanded, which choice would be the most appropriate topic for the new paragraph?
   A. selecting proper kindling
   B. compass navigation in the wilderness
   C. properly extinguishing the fire
   D. items to bring on hikes
   E. places to find tinder

Review

Lessons 19 – 21

EXERCISE I – Inferences

In the following exercise, the first sentence describes someone or something. Infer information from the first sentence, and then choose the word from the Word Bank that best completes the second sentence.

Word Bank

munificent	inept	tyrannical	resilient
pretentious	unassailable	staunch	multifarious

1. The small business could not afford to hire an employee for each specific job, so instead it hired people who had experience in many fields.
   From this sentence, we can infer that the company hires people who have _____ skills.

2. No one could convince Fran that his latest project was a waste of time.
   From this sentence, we can infer that Fran is a[n] _____ believer in his work.

3. The king was known to punish messengers who delivered bad news.
   From this sentence, we can infer that the king is _____.

4. Shannon is never at a loss for ornate and pompous words, especially when she makes herself the subject of the conversation.
   From this sentence, we can infer that Shannon is _____.

5. The waiter fouled up every other order, and spilled beverages on at least two different customers.
   From this sentence, we can infer that the waiter is _____.

EXERCISE II – Related Words

Some of the vocabulary words from lessons 19–21 have related meanings. Complete the following sentences by choosing the word that best completes the specified relationship. Some word pairs will be antonyms, some will be synonyms, and some will be words often used in the same context.

1. *Antagonism* can result if two people have _____ for each other.
    A. doggerel
    B. posterity
    C. disdain
    D. relics
    E. atrophy

2. An *iota* of food was difficult to find after the drought caused a[n] _____ of crops.
    A. imp
    B. rivulet
    C. capsize
    D. dearth
    E. spelunker

3. *Cavalier* is most synonymous with
    A. pretentious.
    B. ardent.
    C. munificent.
    D. embezzle.
    E. sumptuous.

4. The *staunch* supporter had a[n] _____ devotion to the cause.
    A. evanescent
    B. tyrannical
    C. invalid
    D. omnipotent
    E. ardent

5. A *tyrannical* ruler is not likely to be described as
    A. morbid.
    B. cavalier.
    C. devious.
    D. munificent.
    E. precipice.

6. The accident easily could have made her an *invalid*, but she miraculously emerged
   A. omnipotent.
   B. unscathed.
   C. surreal.
   D. inept.
   E. ardent.

7. *Disencumber* is nearly the opposite of
   A. perturb.
   B. pretentious.
   C. capsize.
   D. disdain.
   E. oracle.

8. *Resilient* is most similar in meaning to
   A. inept.
   B. invalid.
   C. atrophy.
   D. unassailable.
   E. evanescent.

9. The state *prosecutes* people who _____ tax money for their own profit.
   A. staunch
   B. perturb
   C. embezzle
   D. thwart
   E. procure

10. She *procured* her collection _____ because the entire set was too expensive to purchase at once.
    A. diatribe
    B. unscathed
    C. resilient
    D. unassailable
    E. piecemeal

EXERCISE III – Crossword Puzzle

Use the clues to complete the crossword puzzle. The answers consist of vocabulary words from lessons 19 through 21.

Across

1. She attributes her _____ to chicken to having eaten it every day during her childhood on the farm.
7. The _____, followed by thousands of shrieking bats, ran out of the cave.
9. If the goalie _____[s], then he or she will not be able to prevent the opposing team from scoring a goal.
10. Tony felt two feet tall after listening to the coach's _____ about players who show up late for practice.
11. Watching six hours of television a day caused the child's mind to

    _____.
13. The famous surgeon was able to _____ the patient of her 100-lb tumor.
14. If the cargo is not stowed properly, the ship might _____.

Down

1. The _____ volunteers worked around the clock without pay to ensure that all the typhoon victims had food and shelter.
2. The villagers _____[d] themselves as the seemingly omnipotent king rode past.
3. He wore the _____ of the United States Marine Corps.
4. The _____ poses riddles, which, when solved, reveal future events.
5. Early mail-order catalogs contained a[n] _____ assortment of goods, from automobiles to houses.
6. The top of the _____ is a dangerous place to be on windy days.
8. A passing security guard _____[ed] the thieves' plan to break into the bank vault.
12. To most people, the broken fragments of clay pottery were junk, but to the archaeologist, the pieces were _____[s] worthy of display in a museum.

EXERCISE III – Crossword Puzzle

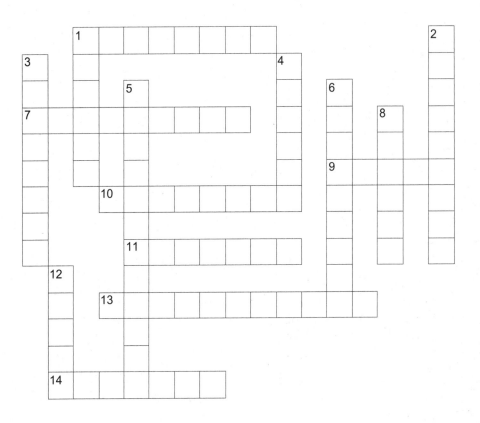